# STATES OF MIND

## FRANCIS STUART

By the same author

*Novels*
Redemption
A Pillar of Cloud
Memorial
Black List: Section H*
A Hole in the Head
The High Consistory

(all published by Martin Brien & O'Keefe.
*available in softback as a King Penguin)

*Poetry*
We have kept the Faith — new and selected poems
(published by the Raven Arts Press)

# STATES OF MIND
Selected Short Prose 1936–1983

## FRANCIS STUART

The Raven Arts Press / Dublin
Martin Brien & O'Keeffe Ltd. / London

19801

This book was first published by

**RAVEN ARTS PRESS**  **MARTIN BRIEN & O'KEEFFE**
31 North Frederick St  78 Coleraine Road
Dublin 1  London SE 3

Francis Stuart
States of Mind
Selected Short Prose 1936–83

ISBN 0 906897 70 X (Raven Arts, softback)
0 906897 71 8 (Raven Arts, hardback)
0 85616 301 5 (Martin Brien & O'Keeffe, hardback)

Coláiste
Mhuire Gan Smál
Luimneach
Class No. 879·89 '4 Stu
Acc. No. 68,440

*Acknowledgements*

Raven Arts Press gratefully acknowledges the financial assistance of the Arts Council /An Chomhairle Ealaíon, Ireland, in the publication of this book, which was also commissioned under the Authors' Royalty Scheme of the Arts Council/An Chomhairle Ealaíon, Ireland.

The author of this book would like to acknowledge the assistance of a Bursary from the Arts Council/An Chomhairle Ealaíon, Ireland, across three years, 1980-1982. Mr. Stuart is now a member of *Aosdána*.

*Acknowledgements are made to the editors of the following, where much of this work has already appeared:*

Firebird 2 (Penguin Books), The Writers: A Sense of Ireland (O'Brien Press), The Irish Times, Envoy (Dublin), New Irish Writing (The Irish Press), Paddy No More (The Wolfhound Press), Adrift (U.S.A.), and The New Statesman (London).

Typeset and designed by Vermilion, Clondalkin, Co Dublin, and printed and bound by Confidential Report Printing. Hardback edition bound by Duffy Bookbinders, Dublin.

# CONTENTS

# PROLOGUE

My autobiographical novel, *BLACK LIST, SECTION H.*, ends
with these sentences: 'Although he was still far from coming to
understand the necessity for what had happend to them. he did
begin to see the silence that he had entered as the deep divide
between the past and what was still to come. Whatever it was
that was at the other end, there was no way of knowing. It
might be a howl of final despair or the profound silence might
be broken by certain words that he didn't yet know how to
listen for.'

Without, I hope, sounding portentous, I think my survival
as a writer is suggested here. It can happen that at the end of
a long novel something becomes clear that was not so at the
start or during the writing.

H (the central figure and in essential ways myself) had a long
way to go before learning how to listen to 'certain words'. In
the first place he had to be granted that space of time and even
then there was no certainty that his path would lead to the
place where those words might be spoken to that fringe of
consciousness from which comes a writer's insights and in-
spiration.

As a survivor from a disaster, or series of disasters, in which
so many had perished, he was under an obligation to remain
faithful to those experiences.

A book of my poems called *WE HAVE KEPT THE FAITH*,
published by *Raven Arts,* spans a lifetime of occasional poetry-
writing. Now in what spans an almost equally long apprentice-
ship in prose, are included some evocations of states of mind,
as well as impressions of long-ago events, that H. had an inkling
that, if he survived, would help him make sense of it all.

Francis Stuart,
Dublin, October 1983.

II

# THE POND

(from *Things to live for*)


Mysterious, emotional, fantastic childhood! Apart from dying, being a child is the only human experience that cannot be told, written about, from first-hand knowledge. For after the lapse of years the knowledge that we have from memory is no longer true and accurate but conditioned and tempered by too much in between. Incidents are recalled, but the essential moods, thoughts, feelings, are forgotten. Only a very few writers like Proust and Tolstoi have recaptured those undertones.

The cawing of crows on a winter evening outside those nursery windows seemed so high meant something to me that no art can explain. Not only that end-of-the-day atmosphere that to a child never loses its sweet sadness, but the end, the eve of something much larger, perhaps of childhood itself, was always suggested by that wild, harsh note. A discordant, unearthly bell tolling the end of the world, an epoch, as the firelight flickered on the wicker-work of a chair that I remember vividly because it, too, had a special significance. It had come, I was told, on the voyage with us from Australia that I did not remember, and so it was a symbol of that past that even then was mysterious and romantic. Looking back at that past within a past, that shadow of a shadow, I come to the confines of life trembling on the verge of a dreamlike chaos out of which I emerged with only that chair as a tangible link, the actual in the midst of the fabulous.

The firelight on the wicker-work, bright yellow round the little dark holes, and the noise of the crows outside from the withering treetops filled me with a sense of time rushing past, of being on the eve of what I only now call, drably, life.

How high, and what ultimate barriers, were those garden walls! How wild and far the countryside beyond them seemed! Under the rhododendron bushes were dark leafy caves smelling damp and sweet with an exciting fragrance. I picked up the gossamer skeletons of leaves and put them in a little box which I buried in the leaf-mould under the bushes. I crumbled the rich brown mould in my hand and heard a few raindrops patter on to the flat polished leaves above me and stayed quite still full of sudden thoughts, that were hardly thoughts so much as feelings, hardly feelings so much as a deep and hushed contemplation. But there again there is no art to describe that childish experience. In order to do so, perhaps one day a new one will be invented.

There was a hum of insects from deep in the shrubbery, but far as I went into it the droning always eluded me. The place from whence it came must be, I thought, the dimmest depths, the most secret spot, but I never found it. It was always there, close at hand, beyond the next bough, and yet when I had stooped under it the noise, low and intense, like the soft beat of drums, was still a little to one side or the other.

One day, in summer, because I remember how leafy it was, I stood by the pond that filled a hollow in a corner of the garden. Although the sun shone, the water looked dark because of the trees, a blue-black sheet. But when I knelt and put my face close to it, it was no longer a sheet at all but transparent with the sunlight, faded a few shades to a deep bronze, falling through it, and I saw the wet pebbles shining at the bottom. Not wet as they were on the gravel after a shower or in my hand after being dipped in water, but with a mysterious perpetual wetness, and sunlit at the same time. There was a bluish shadow on the bronze-coloured floor of the pond, and hanging just above the shadow I saw a fish. Its back was a green-brown, polished and smoother than even the laurel leaves: and its gills opened and closed, and I saw the pink inside when they opened. I caught my breath. I had never before seen anything so strange and remote. Its tail was moving with a slow rhythmic sway, and beneath it the shadow trembled but did not vanish.

In my ears there was the whisper of the leaves in the summer breeze, and in my nostrils the smell of the water, cold and slightly bitter in the sweet warm air. The stones on which I knelt were hurting my knees, but I did not move. A leaf floated past curved at its tip like the prow of a picture book boat. But I knew I was far from picture-books and make-believe. I was on the fringe of reality. I was happy and a little frightened. And I somehow knew that that was the only way to be happy; that happiness without a touch of fear, of awe, is not happiness at all but contentment. I could not have said that, but I knew it. I knew that something in the unexpected smell of the water, in the little harsh noise of the leaves, in the faint movement of the fish's tail frightened me and at the same time was the cause of my joy.

When I got up my knees hurt and I was dizzy with stooping and there was the imprint of the gravel on the soft palm of my hands, but a door had been opened to me, a secret revealed. I could not have said what that secret was, and I cannot say now. But I know that it was the first glimpse I had into life, beautiful in its terrible passivity, delicate and intricate with a savage strength. And although I had a secret joy, from then that seed of discontent was perhaps sown in me. My feet were then set on that quest, that pilgrimage that, with so much straying from the way, they are still bent on. I had started in search of that reality that cannot be counterfeited, that is stark and cold and harsh like the smell of water and the noise of leaves. But it was a long time before I learned, if I have even now learnt, that it cannot be counterfeited.

1936

# REVELATIONS

As a boy when so much seemed to be happening, it was not easy to grasp what was going to be vital and what would quickly fade. When he heard the news of the February Revolution in Russia it was from the matron of Rugby School sanatorium where he was recovering from what was probably some psychosomatic complaint, and who had come into the ward to deliver letters sent over from their resident houses to the patients.

The envelope with the Co. Antrim postmark took his primary attention and he hardly took in what she was telling them about the Tsar having been deposed. The letter was from his cousin, Anita, who rather than her younger sister who was his own age, had been his special companion during the Christmas holidays and was now at home for good, having finished her schooling.

He saw at a glance that all was well, nothing had changed between them. He was still her 'darling Toby' (he had been christened Tobit) and it had been raining all the time since he had left his mother's country house, a few miles from her own family's (raining in her heart, could that be what she meant?). But further on she wrote more boldly, hinting at all kinds of things that made him breathless. When she and her young brother, whom she was accompanying back to his school at Cheltenham had got off the train that was taking him to Rugby, the station had been full of soldiers returning to the front and some womenfolk were there to see them off. During the wait for their connection, her young brother had spotted a woman with a baby at her breast. Anita wrote: 'Charlie was staring at her so greedily that she called out: "Want a drop too, dearie?" I pretended I had nothing to do with him.'

This too was in code like about the rain, a secret message addressed to him, concerning the mystery of which she knew much more than he. He put the letter back in the envelope and packed it under his pillow.

The news that the matron had brought them was also in code; it was not just that the Tsar had been deposed, and that has a phrase in the history books, but behind it was the real news that had not yet leaked out and perhaps never would. This was to do with him as much as with the Tsar, a revolution having broken out in his vicinity too, but not deposing him, on the contrary seeming to free him from what was a sort of prison. It had begun when he had read, in one of the magazines on display, along with a couple of daily papers, on the table near the entry to his house-master's apartments off the stone-flagged corridor, a translation of a poem of Mayakovsky's called 'The Cloud in Trousers.' He knew that something new was happening and not only in far-away Russia, and that, if all went well, he, Tobit, would have his part in it.

But at the moment he was more taken with the prospect of answering his cousin's letter and trying to respond to her coded messages with some of his own.

As if all this was not enough, there was the reappearance in the Spring of 'Gay Crusader' to which to look forward. In *The Sporting Times,* which he bought at a newsagent's in a part of the town that was out of bounds and smuggled into his study, he had read that this three-year-old, that had made such an impression when winning the Criterion Stakes at Newmarket the previous autumn, would soon have his first outing of the new season on the same course. Based on a careful study of the yellow pages of the paper he kept hidden, with Anita's letters, in the pigeon holes of his big roll-top desk, but also on a certain sort of presentiment, he believed that this was one of the classic colts that would win one or more of the big prizes.

Back in his house (E.A. St. Hill's) from the sanitorium, his private concerns were taking up so much of Tobit's time that though he had a knack of slipping through the classes on a minimum of actual attention, the mid-term report from his form-masters to the headmaster, the Rev. E. E. Davids, D.D., caused him to receive one of the dreaded summonses. These could, in some cases, end in one of the mini executions carried out by the Doctor of Divinity with the notorious birch, while the School House porter, wearing full livery, stood beside the victim who was bent over the block, presumably a table, with trousers down. Afterwards, it was reported, the porter extracted the twig splinters from the semi-executed's striped and blood-oozing bottom.

Dr. Davids, all in black, received him in his study at the top of the ancient tower at one corner of the school quadrangle.

— Very disappointing reports, Spokane (Tobit's surname sometimes seemed to him as burdensome as his first). All speak of a casual attitude, in some cases bordering on contempt. Several mention indifference, though all agree that you show flashes of ability that are evidence that you could do much better if putting your mind to it.

A pause, hesitation, a blanching of the face that Tobit could achieve at will, though indeed he had heard enough to bring it about naturally.

— Well, Spokane?

— It's the war, Sir.

— The war?

— The death toll.

— You have lost a brother?

— I'm an only child, my father died shortly after my birth. It was a cousin, Sir, but like a brother.

— Would it be painful to tell me the circumstances?

— Missing since the Somme, presumed dead, in the R.F.C., Sir. His crashed plane was found after our advance and the propellor was sent home to my uncle and aunt.

These facts were true, but, although he had seen a lot of Anita's brother, Jamie Spokane, they had not been all that close.

Dr. Davids sat a moment or two with closed eyes and Tobit himself for the first time felt a deep distress at Jamie's death.

— I am glad you confided in me, Spokane. I shall ask your form masters to make some special allowances, without, of course, mentioning what you have told me in detail. At the same time, I believe if you bring a little more application to your work it need not distract you from continuing to cherish your cousin's memory.

Jamie's memory! He resolved to cherish it from now on, in the midst of all the other preoccupations he could now turn his thoughts to without too much danger.

# THE WATER GARDEN

As a child I spent a season in hell, along with Rimbaud, not to mention some of the others, without my nearest and dearest having an inkling of the situation, or that such a sojourn was possible.

I once overheard the doctor say to my mother: 'A moody neurotic boy, Mrs. Grimes. You should discourage what you tell me is all the mooning around and staring out of the window for hours on end.'

A menagerie used sometimes to stop in our town, managed by a foreigner called Olhausen, and it both attracted me and plunged me anew into pain and anxiety on behalf of the caged creatures. A little later, Mr. Olhausen gave up his travelling show and opened a pet store a few streets away from our house.

Having often seen me with my nose glued to his shop window, in all weathers, rain or shine, the old fellow called me in one day and gave me a small acquarium in which was a miniature jungle of water plants and five tiny fish.

— They get all the nourishment they need from the vegetation which grows as fast as they feed on it, so this little water garden, like the big world outside, if they'd only leave it alone, is self-contained and self-propagating.

I got the sense of what he said, if not exactly grasping the meaning of some individual words and phrases.

I kept the tank, more of a glass bowl really, on the table by the window in my room to which I went after the wear and tear of the day (I attended a local school where I didn't shine, needless to say, though why 'nedless' if it comes to that?) to watch the fish at dusk.

I lay on my bed exhausted (the piano lessons had gone badly

*17*

as usual) following the deceptively random movements of the tiny dust-coloured, though momentarily gleaming, creatures among the water weeds. They swam to a rythmic pattern that I slowly learnt to follow and decipher, and, God knows, this was a comfort to me. But there were inevitable gaps in my knowledge of the water-woven tapestry, because they swam all night while I slept, of lay awake without being able to see them anymore. In the daytime they floated motionless among the plants where they were hidden altogether.

— The company he keeps, that's very important, Mrs. Grimes.

Now, I knew, I had the company needed, though I kept it to myself.

My mother wanted to know if I was going to put some goldfish in the tank.

— The ones I have are O.K.

— But you haven't any as far as I can make out.

— I wouldn't say that, you know.

But she didn't know. Anyhow, I wasn't going to invite her up to my room of an evening when there was a better chance of seeing something.

In those days I wanted to become a musician, perhaps a concert violinist, and the piano lessons were the nearest I could come to preparing myself until the red-haired girl who was teaching me said I was tone deaf, which disposed both of violin and piano.

I persevered on my own, reading all the books on musical themes I could find, and even biographies of the great composers, as if they could affect my musical talent, or its absence, one way or the other. In one of the latter I came on this: 'A state of reconciliation and relief, as after immense suffering, is produced by Beethoven's *Quartet in A Minor.*

Here was my secret state, when watching the minute, colourless coldwater creatures at their mysterious task, fully and openly expressed! I was amazed and shocked, and also reassured. I couldn't, of course, have myself put it like that, or put it at all, come to that.

I am recalling as simply and honestly as I can these early events in order to make clear why the frustration of having to give up the dream of becoming a concert violinist, let alone a composer, didn't exactly cast me down. And likewise why I was able to abandon my later less pure ambition of gaining fame and acclamation as a painter.

In another book, not about music this time, I read that if I happened to know (I took all precepts I came on as addressed to me personally) that a priceless pearl was buried under a certain heap of rubble. I should sell all I had (my artistic talents, such as they were) and buy the plot or site. Naturally, the writer didn't know that it had already been bestowed on me for nothing, in the form of the aquarium.

In later years, indeed only a couple of years ago, I made my only enquiry, a mistaken one at that, about the fish, apart, that is, from poring over books on various aquatic creatures and natural history in general. I put some hesitant questions to Mr. Olhausen's son.

— My old fellow, a showman to the last, used to display, beside a bowl of water in the shop window, a notice advertising what he called the world-renowned Japanese invisible Kra fish.

— I never saw anything like that there.

— Perhaps you were too young to read, Mr. Grimes.

— Your father impressed me as . . .

But there was no point in discussing old Oldhausen with his son, who evidently thought him capable of gimmicks. A child knows these things better, whatever else he is ignorant of, whether he can read or do sums; indeed, his intuition is the sharper just because his mind isn't cluttered up with a lot of information, either useless or untrue.

Was there ever an age when the citizens were exposed to so much lies and bullshit? asked a close friend the other day, who looks up to me as an amateur historian.

After the abortive musical interlude, I dreamed, for a time, of receiving letters in foreign languages from Keepers of Art in Continental galleries, enquiring as to the mythological significance of certain paintings of mine. And, who knows, I might even have made such aspirations come true. Instead of which, I abandoned them, as well as other dreams, addictions and flirtations, not to mention drink and television, made a clean sweep of the lot, not from moral principles, but because I was being distracted from the evening vigils.

Vigils that all these years later, and although the miniature aquarium is gone, I still meditate on, and shall continue to do so, not so much with an open, as a loving, mind.

Here I am then, an old man, far from illustrious, without

achievements to fall back on, ill-educated, and still known for the company he keeps.

What sort? According to some, to almost everybody around in fact, the town's riff-raff, the section of the criminal element not yet apprehended by the responsible authorities, besides those who have served their just punishments and remain unrepentent and unreformed.

According to me? Oh, I couldn't define my companions morally. I don't understand terms and strictures of that sort. Riff-raff? So what? They consist of some violent characters, some who are passionate, a few really vicious, all failures in society's eyes, like myself, and, though they in no way stand out from the others, two or three truly loving souls.

# VOLODYA

One evening in the early autumn of 1922 he took the boat to Liverpool with a bundle of notes, a sheet headed Óglaigh na hÉireann followed, in bracket, by 'The Irish Volunteers' and a typed shopping list for specific types of small arms. The idea of carrying the money and documents anywhere but in his jacket pocket did not occur to him.

The civil war was a few months old and Simeon, partly because of his air of youthful gaucherie, his Australian passport and his being involved in previous armed activity, had been asked by the commander of a country column, then lying wounded in a house in Dublin, to undertake the mission.

With his two smart-looking, almost empty suitcases, only one of which he himself was to return with fully packed, he took a train across the grimy English midlands to Hull.

As he sailed down the Humber estuary on a ship bound for Ostend with late holiday makers, he sought out the Purser; not on a sudden impulse but driven by a compulsion that had been at the fringe of his consciousness (never fully acknowledged) ever since he had agreed to the trip. Was it, he wondered, one of those crazy but necessary impulses (necessary to a pattern he couldn't decipher) that at times possessed him and that had been behind his ridiculously early and hurried marriage?

The bearded sailor in braided uniform was helpful and unexpecedly sympathetic, perhaps welcoming a change from the usual tourist enquiries. He consulted a directory in his tiny office and gave Simeon an address in Brussels of a trade mission rather than a consulate, which Simeon, thanking him, stowed away with the rest in his inside pocket. He was still uncommitted.

When, however, the train from Ostend stopped at Ghent

(Gand), instead of alighting on the platform that smelt of cigars, he closed his eyes and sat back in his corner seat. In Brussels he left the cases at the station and took a taxi to the address in the rue de l'Ecuyer.

After a wait in an anteroom, he was taken into an office whose walls were covered with posters depicting industrial scenes in the Soviet Union, that had captions in French and Russian. A frozen-faced official at a desk listened to Simeon's explanation, in a mixture of French and English and showed no sign of understanding either, but let him continue to the end, at which point a young woman from another desk butted in. In a French that Simeon understood fairly well, indicating, he thought, that it wasn't her native tongue, she mentioned somebody called Elsa Triolet whom she was going to telephone in Paris. Leaving him with a volume of English translations of poems by Essenin and Mayakovsky, she then left the room.

He supposed that she'd mentioned the name of her friend in Paris whom she'd no doubt an appointment to phone at a stated time, so that he should not think she'd gone off in the hope that her stern-faced colleague would get rid of him, or at least to let him cool his heels, as they say, and rethink his preposterous request.

When she returned, though, she told him that she hadn't been able to get hold of the mysterious Elsa who, as he may not have heard, had recently left her husband, Mr. Triolet, but that he needn't worry on that account (on which account? Surely not about the separation of a couple of whom he'd first heard ten minutes ago? Presumably about the helpful young woman's failure to contact her). She had heard that Mayakovsky was at this very time in Berlin with Elsa's sister, where she wouldn't be at all surprised if Elsa hadn't joined them, though her informant (the unhappy M. Triolet? but there was no use his trying to guess when he was so out of his depth) hadn't said so.

She gave him the name of the hotel where the famous young Russian was staying. All he had to do now was to obtain an authorisation from the Allied Occupation Commission to pass through their zone in Germany and possibly a German visa, of that she wasn't sure.

All went unexpecedly smoothly, though getting the stamps on his passport delayed him in Brussels a couple of days. On the evening of the third he arrived at the Bahnhof-am-Zoo in Berlin and took a taxi straight to the address he'd been given.

Simeon was somewhat disappointed at the look of the hotel and of the street in which it was situated, but for all he knew, the great Russian revolutionary might not wish to draw attention to himself by appearing in one of the grander places. Or indeed, he had just thought of that, it might be in accord with Soviet principles.

In a sentence he'd prepared in German, he asked at the desk that a note he had written in English should be taken to Herr Mayakovsky. The fat, bald-headed manager, or perhaps owner, took it without comment and disappeared up the stairs.

Simeon, as was his habit, spent the time of waiting in vivid imaginings of possible outcomes.

A. A swift return of *le Patron,* or rather, *Mein Wirt,* with a brusque intimation that the distinguished Russian gentleman did not receive every Tom, Dick and Harry who happened to be at a loose end.

B. A message that Simeon should return the next day, or the one after, which would mean kicking his heels around Berlin while the money entrusted to him for a quite different purpose dwindled.

C. A request that he ascend to Mayakovsky's apartment without a moment's delay.

As always, none of these forecasts were fulfilled.

Instead, a pale, dark girl with glowing eyes (years later Simeon recalled these eyes when coming on a book of verse by her second husband, Louis Aragon, called *'Les Yeux d'Elsa')* came down to meet him.

She greeted him in almost perfect English and began chatting away as if they knew each other quite well and that this was a friendly call on her. When Simeon at last put a tentative question as to whether Maykovsky was staying at the hotel, she said: 'Volodya? Oh, he's deep in a poker session that's been going on since early morning for high stakes.'

— When is it likely to end?

— There's no telling. Since he arrived here a week ago he's seen nothing of Berlin. He spends all day and half the night playing cards up in his bedroom with some Moscow friends.

Simeon made no direct comment but asked Elsa how she spent her time.

— Oh, we shop, Lili and I. You've no idea if you've only just arrived of what can be bought here for almost nothing because of the inflation. You'll no doubt be fitting yourself out in style.

Little she knew the pangs of guilt that he already was feeling on leaving the Republicans at home in the lurch, as it was, without finally destroying all possiblity of excuse on his return by buying suits (did she notice the frayed cuffs of his jacket?) and whatever took his fancy in this city where he should never have been in the first place!

Elsa chatted away, mentioning by Christian name members of the entourage whose relationship he couldn't sort out.

What about seeing how the card-game was progressing, he hesitantly suggested.

She returned after some delay, which Simeon had taken as a hopeful sign, wearing a fur coat that she told him she and Lili had picked up for the equivalent of one dollar.

No news from the Poker session?

– Oh Yes, Volodya asks you to meet him tomorrow in the *Romanisches Café* at six o'clock.

Another whole day wasted and the supply of small arms to be delivered to the hard-pressed Republicans dwindling by the hour!

He found a room in a hotel, went to bed early, spent the next morning at the zoological gardens, had a frugal midday meal of Bockwurst and potato salad, and arrived at the rendezvous, situated where the city's principal thoroughfares meet at the *Gedächtnis Kirke,* outside which two tall, late sunflowers were still in bloom, at five minutes past the appointed hour.

Once through the revolving door, the first person he caught sight of was Elsa, still in her fur coat although the heating seemed more than adequate.

Could the tall young man with the cropped head of a convict and the rather scowling expression be Mayakovsky? Yes, it was, and hardly had Elsa introduced them than Simeon was in his bearlike embrace. There was also Lili Brik, the poet's beloved, as she had explained at the hotel, and Osya, Lili's bald husband, as well as Ilya Ehrenberg.

Released, Simeon sat on a chair between Mayakovsky and Elsa and with an expansive, clumsy gesture the poet beckoned a waiter and growled out an order for two bottles of champagne.

After all this it seemed to Simeon an anti-climax to come out with his prepared speech of fraternal greetings, etc., instead of which, with Elsa as interpreter, he managed impromptu, an expression of homage to this man whose poems (the few he had come across) had lit for him some very dark days.

Having seen and spoken with his Russian hero, Simeon decided to return to Brussels by the train that he'd found out left that night. The next morning in Ghent at the dealer's to whom he had the written introduction he'd buy whatever guns with what remained of the money allowed, and make for home with the one sparsely filled case.

He played with the notion of a tale about being forewarned of a search of luggage at the Liverpool boat and his being forced to discard most of the weapons, salvaging only what he could dispose about his person. However, to give him his due, he never seriously entertained the idea.

Mayakovsky had his own ideas (about Simeon's early departure) and with unexpected old-fashioned formality invited him to dinner at Stöcklers.

— Just the two of us, old soldier, with Elsa (who was translating the words) who is angry with me just now, as go-between. And, of course, my sweetest Lissik; possibly Shklovsky too.

Who these last two were Simeon had no idea until Elsa told him that Lissik was one of the endless variations Mayakovsky liked to play on her sister's name. Victor Shklovsky was a Russian emigré living in Berlin.

In the end, Simeon confided in Mayakovsky, whom, like the others, he was now calling Volodya, the true state of his affairs.

The big poet clapped a hand to his brow.

— I guessed there were complications from your worried air the moment I laid eyes on you. God preserve us, you're living under pressures as great as my own! Your beleagured comrades will not be exposed to the common enemy while we celebrate our happy meeting! You will catch the early morning express with enough good Soviet roubles, which you can change legally in Belgium, to purchase all the guns originally on your list, and one word of advice from a seasoned campaigner: don't neglect to add a few mausers, invaluable in a tight corner, I assure you.

Simeon dined with Vladimir Mayakovsky and a half-dozen others in a fashionable restaurant on Kurfurstendamm on a mild October night in 1922, on turtle soup, langoustine and rasp-

25

berry compote, a bundle of paper roubles, engraved with Lenin's head, stowed away in his pocket, drinking French wine, his host disdaining Rhine and Moselle.

# From THINGS TO LIVE FOR

I remember in Maryborough prison Paddy coming back into our cell after he had been for a week in the prison hospital. He came in stooping under the blanket that I had hung across the doorway to replace the burnt door and sat down on a box. It was a cold morning in the winter of 1922 and I was lying on some loose planks under a couple of verminous blankets.

"They shot Joe this morning," Paddy said, referring to a boy we had both known and who had been with Paddy through the civil war.

"I heard them," I said. "There were two volleys."

"I saw them shot," he said, "they killed them the other side of the hospital wing. I looked all the time. There were three of our lads. It was pouring rain."

"Did you know the others?" I asked.

"No. They came out without hats and I noticed Joe hadn't bothered to lace his boots all the way up. It must be funny putting on your boots and knowing you'll never take them off again. There was an officer with a gun in his hand walking beside them. It was very muddy in the yard. The other two boys had rosary beads hanging from their hands, but Joe had his hands in his pockets. When they came to the wall they turned round and the two boys put the beads over their heads so that they hung round their necks. Then they stood to attention but Joe kept his hands in his pockets and his shoulders hunched up. The sergeant said something to him and he shook his head. Then the sergeant stepped back and took the gun out of his holster. The firing squad was standing about fifteen paces away. When the officer gave the word they brought up their rifles to their shoulders. The two boys had their eyes shut and Joe was looking at the mud just in front of his boots. There were tears

streaming down the face of one of the boys from under his shut
eyelids. There was the rain on their faces too but I saw the
tears. When the soldiers fired to put up his hands to his chest
and tore at his coat as though he wanted to open it. He swayed
forward without falling. His coat came open with the buttons
ripped off and the blood ran down his hands. Then he fell on
his knees with his head bowed over the other boy who had
fallen sideways, hisface in a pool. Joe had fallen back against
the wall but his feet were still on the ground and he was
choking with blood and spittle coming out of his mouth and his
face turning dark. The other boy fell from his kness and the two
boys lay one across the other. The sergeant put his gun to the
side of Joe's head and fired four or five shots into it. The side of
his head was torn open; then he fell sideways with his shoulders
slipping down along the wall."

We talked about death and wondered how it would come to
each of us.

"Perhaps like that, too," I said.

"I want about ten years of life after we get out of here,"
Paddy said, "and then I don't mind. I want to find the best
things and do them and then not cling to them, but go on."

# A BERLIN DIARY
kept intermittently between 1940 and 1945

*After the arrest at the end of 1942 and, as I learnt later, the execution of the Schultze-Boysens who were friends of mine, members of the pro-Russian "Rote Kapelle" underground group, I destroyed some of these notebooks that might have been compromising had my flat been searched. The extracts that I later rewrote from memory are approximately dated, the others are direct from surviving notebooks.*

*February 18, 1940. Pension Naumann, Nikolsburger Platz.*
Was asked by Dr. Haferkorn of the Auswertiges Amt (Foreign Office) if I would write some talks for William Joyce (known at home and in England, but not here, as Lord Haw-Haw). Incidentally, I recall Liam's [1] remark to me at the Royal Hotel, Glendalough, that "he was winning the war for Germany single-handed."

I agreed and wrote three, the first of which Joyce will broadcast tonight and, as I have no radio, have arranged with William Warnock [2] to spend the evening with him at our Legation and listen to it there.

The theme of my contributions, which I know is not exactly what either the Germans nor Joyce want, is a recollection of some historic acts of aggression on part on the United Kingdom, similar to those which British propagana is denouncing the Nazis for.

*Autumn, 1940.*
A telephone call from Cudahy's [4] secretary inviting me to the Hotel Adlon, where he is staying, for a drink.

We had a long talk and quite a few drinks yesterday in his room there. He told me he had interviewed Hitler a few days ago at the Chancellery for the New York paper that he now represents. Before leaving he had advised the Fuehrer that torpedoing American ships was increasing anti-German feeling and could, if continued, bring the United States into the war, for which Churchill is hoping.

I said that if the British Intelligence Service got to know of what he had suggested and feared there might be another interview, his life might be in danger.

But Cudahy laughed at the idea and siad I was living in the world of PIGEON IRISH (an early novel of mine in which I had prophesised a war in some ways similar to this). He told me he had in fact asked for another meeting with Hitler when he came back from Berlin after a holiday he was planning.

He then suggested, if he received permission from the Chancellery, that I might like to accompany him. He added that he had mentioned me there as an Irish writer of great promise who was in Germany as a neutral observer.

After all the champagne cocktails, I agreed at once.

This morning I felt rather differently. By being taken along· and granted an audience, for that is what it came to, I could lose some of what I still considered my spirit of independence as an imaginative writer, though others might think I had forfeited that already.

This idea obsessed me and prevented me concentrating on my talk at the university. I did not dare telephone Cudahy and explain what I felt, as I supposed calls to him would be monitored. So I shall call round in the next day or two.

*Autumn, 1940.*
Have just read of Cudahy's death in Switzerland. No details were given.

*Autumn, 1940.*
Eileen Walsh (who works at the Irish Legation) brought me a bundle of *Irish Independents*. Nothing about Cudahy, through some copies of around the relevant date were missing.

There was no doubt that power of the kind that is centered in Hitler, largely corrupt power, had a fascination for certain writers. I am thinking of Cromwell's attraction for Milton, Napeolon's for several contemporary poets.

*August, 1940.*
Met Colonel von Stauffenberg [5] by appointment in the Hotel Eden to put before him some of the complaints of individual prisoners-of-war I had talked to in camps in occupied Poland which I visited with Colonel Curtin. These were not all Irish, in fact the most moving appeal came from an English sergeant on behalf of his men incarcerated in a damp cavern of a room in a former fortress near Posen (the Polish Poznan).

Stauffenberg, delicately built, limping from an old wound, speaking perfect English, listened sympathetically and said that conditions in the camps were improving and would soon meet the requirements of the International Red Cross regulations.

He is obviously highly intelligent and not one of the habitual prevaricators.

*April, 1941.*
A party at the Weissenborns [6] last night from which I have not yet recovered. The most lavish affair I've been at during the war, with all kinds of drinks from champagne to exotic schnapps from the Balkans. Met Lieutenant Schultze-Boysen and his wife. Libertas, a young couple of pronounced liberal views which they didn't hide, also Lala Andersen, a Scandinavian who first sang "Lili Marlene" at a variety theatre on Kurfurstendamm not so long ago, and the publisher Rowolt, head of, it seems, what had been one of the few progressive firms before the final clamp-down. He and the Schultze-Boysens agreed that if Hitler won the war there might well be a certain relaxation of state control, and it was semi-seriously suggested that the Tiergarten might become a kind of Berlin Hyde Park with its Speakers' Corner for the airing of dissident views.

The Weissenborns have an elegant top-floor flat in Nurnberger Strasse. One of his novels, *Das Madchen von Fäno,* has been made into a film with the beautiful Hungarian actress, Brigitte Horney, in the star part.

In the bathroom Rowolt and I noticed what we both took to be a briquette on the glass-topped table and, with a drunken idea of being orderly, deposited it in the lavatory bowl and pressed the lever but could not flush it away. This morning I realise it was, of course, a hair brush.

*Late Summer, 1941*
A visit from Kurt Haller [3] a few days ago. He asked me this rather surprising question: Was I willing and ready to sail with a German sea-captan, Nielsen, known to his wide circle of friends by the affectionate pseudonym of "Heinz Mück" (legendary German adventurer), in a Breton fishing boat with a small crew, disguised as French fishermen, to Ireland? I was to act as a kind of advance link between the I.R.A. and two unnamed Irishmen, both prominent Republicans, who would be shortly landed in Ireland. (These two were Helmut Clissman and Frank Ryan, though I did not know this at the time).

My first impulse was to refuse. I had travelled to Germany with considerable difficulty in the early days of the war, and had no reason to return home so soon. But I had two compelling reasons to agree: First, because I have always believed in accepting opportunities to new adventure and experience, and, second, because, had I declined, I believed I would go down in Haller's estimation as another of the timid civilian intellectuals.

I told him, yes, I would go, and asked what he thought would happen if we were intercepted by a British warship, a contingency that I saw as quite likely.

"Captain Neilsen will scuttle the craft."

Some weeks later (though this is not recorded in the Berlin Diaries) Haller returned to tell me the plan had been abandoned. (I never learned why). And shortly after that he informed me of Russell's death on the submarine and Ryan's return in it to Germany, adding that Ryan had asked to see me.

*March 14, 1942. 13 Rankestrasse.*
The heat coming on in radiator again after some days without. A cold, wintry evening with piles of shovelled, frozen snow at the edges of the blackened-out streets with only small, blue-violet glimmers of light far away at the top of the lamp standards. But how intense the atmosphere of these days and nights and how immersed in them I am!

I dreamt the other day that I had left here and no longer heard German spoken; I knew I couldn't get back and I felt I had lost something infinitely precious.

The few potatoes, my ration for supper, are boiling on the much-mended electric ring.

*July 11, 1942.*
Reading some Irish papers of April and May that Eileen Walsh brought me. I was shocked by the dominant clericalism. I had forgotten that it is as impossible to criticise publicly the Catholic Church and its clergy at home as here the National Socialist ideology. Men of the utmost ignorance and inner emptiness (as I have learnt many of them are) are honoured and given prominence in at least two of the Dublin dailies.

The people who know nothing of the spiritual struggle, courage, passion and humility without which religion is merely submission to authority, churchgoing and respectability, set much of the tone of life in Ireland. They fear and despise art.

My work at the university is often a nervous strain. The debate class means trying to get a few silent girl students to open their mouths about some God-forsaken subject and keeping this up for three-quarters of an hour.

*August 1, 1942.*
A very hot day again after a long break in the weather. Wrote the first of weekly talks to broadcast to Ireland. Had lunch with Frank (Ryan) and discussed these with him. He agreed that they must not be propaganda in the sense that the flood of war journalism from all sides has become, and that, of course, they must support our neutrality. He suggested, and I fully agreed, that there must be no anti-Russian bias.

*August 5, 1942.*
Yesterday at the Sacrower See with S, Frank and Helmut (Clissman). In and out of the lake in the oppressive heat, between times drinking wine in the restaurant in the wood.

*Berlin, Sunday, August 9th, 1942.*
A letter from Sam Beckett in Paris which I was very glad to get. He says he has nearly finished a novel, that's to say he had done the first chapter or two. I undertand that: once the definitive beginning is made after long meditation and false starts, a great deal has been accomplished. He seems to be living there even more cut off and isolated than I am.

The nearer one comes to the huge melodrama of the war, the

more alone one feels and appalled at the parts being played by almost all the principal characters: Churchill, Stalin, Hitler, the Rossevelts, Timoschenko, Pétain, de Gaulle, General Giraud, Mussolini, Count Ciano. Which will be remembered with any respect? Churchill, possibly, and I think Gandhi in his Indian hermitage. Stalin is the most mysterious and 'all have their place 'i the story.'

Wisdon has retreated into hidden lairs. Wisdon and peace are only to be come on these days in poetry which I feel the need to read more than ever before. That of Keats especially.

Keats in Italy. I can't imagine greater suffering than those four months or so. Illness of lungs and stomach, Fanny Brawne lost for ever, his work left in the beginning, publicly despised. What state of poetic wisdom had Keats reached by the time of his death!

It is only those who can be content for long periods alone in their room who are fit to rule.

## August 23, 1942

Yesterday went to see Cremin at our Legation who told me that he had now received instructions from the government not to renew my passport. He personally was very nice over this unfortunate business and said he would make another request stressing the difficulties of my position which, as things get worse, would increase.

And a few days ago had a letter from Scherl [7] saying the Propaganda Ministry had refused them permission to publish a German translation of my novel, "Winter Song".

This book could not now be published in England, or the U.S.A. either, as I am well aware, although in no way political.

The first serious British attempt to land in France seems to have been something of a disaster and was no doubt only made reluctantly after Churchill's visit to Moscow at the cost of probably thousands of lives, mostly Canadian.

## August 30, 1942

Watching a lone Russian plane last night flying very slowly against the clear evening sky, though that was an illusion caused by its great height. A softly glowing, gently moving star with the red and white rosettes of the Flak scattered round it. I could see it for several minutes, praying it would not be hit as it came in from the east, passed behind the two poplar trees in front of the balcony of this suburban flat, and then turned south and sailed away.

Alone, and from what a mysterious distance!

Wrote a talk on the six men condenmned to death in Belfast for broadcasting tonight.

Another hot evening. From the garden of the house opposite come the reassuring cackle of ducks, and I think of the commons at Duleek with Bellewstown Hill on the quiet horizon.

Am leaving this apartment that I have had the loan of to-morrow.

*Vienna, September 1942.*

It is almost impossible at times to forget the war here. The streets are lit until ten, the restaurants and cafés are full, a few, the more expensive, do not bother to demand ration coupons. In ten days I have not read a newspaper nor listened to the radio.

We spend time in the galleries, lingering at some of the paintings such as that by Pereda of the angel with dark wings. An angel of death? Also of peace. Also a fine nude by him, wingless but with the same ambiguity. Walking in the Vienna Woods, crossing the ravine between the Kahlenberg and Leopoldberg, reminding me of a Wicklow glen and stepping from stone to stone over a stream at home.

At Friendenau races, the old wooden stands, the paint faded and peeling, the imperial eagle still on the emperor's box. One of our last evenings sitting in the dusk in St. Stefan's cathedral, the windows glowing high above and Bach being played.

Bought a store of typing paper which is unobtainable in Berlin, some wine and a teapot.

*Berlin, Sept. 17th, 1942.*

A message came through from Hempel saying my radio comments on the Belfast death sentences had 'gute Wirkung.' (a good effect). If my talks have even a minute influence in helping to keep our neutrality they aren't just waste, as I often think.

Read this from Keats:

And other spirits there are standing apart
Upon the forehead of the age to come;
These, these will give the world another heart,
And other pulses. Hear ye not the hum
Of mighty workings in some distant Mart?
Listen awhile ye nations and be dumb.

Keats could not imagine the evil that has overtaken us. The forehead of the age to come looks like being marked by degradation. No matter who wins the war the world (Europe) is unlikely to be better than before. Twenty-five or thirty years from now it may well be in a worse state than in the last years of peace.

*Sept. 29th, 1942.*
Pouring all day. Reading Keats. Of a poem of Wordsworth he writes in a letter: 'he was in a too comfortable a mood when he wrote it.' This applies to most of what was being written before the war. 'Like a whale's back in a sea of prose,' he says of a sentence he liked in a boring book.

At first Keats lived in his vision of beauty and 'Poesy'. Then he lost it and was overwhelmed by darkness and the world. Later, through suffering, he rediscovered the principle, but this time of the beauty of all things, even in suffering. From this period come his finest poems including one called 'Purgatory Blind.'

This was his 'Vast Idea'. Without Keats it would be difficult to preserve any sense of calm some of these days.

*December 19, 1942.*
Was shown an April number of the illustrated English weekly, *Picture Post,* in which it said the Irish were not impressed by my promises. What promises for heaven's sake. But I shall have to get used to worse than that and from more serious critics.

Mentioned the fact of the refusal by Irish government to renew my passport in my weekly broadcast talk and showed it to Hartmann [8] who rang just now and said it would have to be taken out because the British must not get to know of it.

For all I know it may have been done on the advice of the British.

*January 27, 1943.*
Went with S. yesterday to visit Frank [9] in the Charité Hospital at lunch time. He was still very ill, eyes veiled, left arm partially paralysed. Hard to say whether he liked being visited, but I think so, as long as we didn't stay long. Doors unlocked, re-locked. Other patients in convict-like uniform.

The food, he said, very bad. He lies there day after day, with one other patient in the room, does not read much, and that till the end of February perhaps.

He told me that McAteer had applied to come here after his recent escape from prison in Belfast and that, he, Frank, had heard this in Copenhagen. I suggested that, if so, it must have been before his, McAteer's, arrest, but I saw that Frank was unable to take in these considerations.

Later I rang Haller and arranged to meet him on Friday to talk about Frank, as well as some other things. Would have got in touch with Helmut but it seems he is in Coperhagen.

*Berlin, November 23rd, 1943.*
S's [10] birthday. One of the worst air-raids so far. We were finishing the evening meal to sound of flak and distant explosions when a heavy blast shattered the glass in the window behind the blackout curtains, blew open the sitting-room door and blew out the rags that were stuffed in the cracks between the wall and the other door to keep out the draft. Thinking perhaps the block had been hit, we went to the cellar. The loud detonations continued for half-an-hour.

Later, on the roof with Martin trying to keep the flames from the burning school next door from setting fire to our roof, he throwing water from the buckets as I handed them to him as they were passed to me from below. Wore a gas mask against the thick smoke. Blazing houses all around and a strong wind, probably caused by the suction of the flames.

*November 26th, 1943.*
An eeriness living amid burnt-out houses, especially at night. The ruins in the darkness and the waiting. The not knowing the immediate future, a kind of widening of the future. At first this made me apprehensive and rather miserable but now those feelings are gone. I don't think of how it will be in the next bad attack (on this quarter) but am very conscious of the

quiet while it lasts. Even a leaf silently and slowly falling is now wonderful. And how much is made of the moon! The other night when there was a moon again, one of the girls came in to tell us' 'Der Mond steht hoch und klar.' (The moon is high and clear). We ran out into the street to see it, perhaps three days old, shining through a gap in the wall of a ruined house.

*March 18th, 1944.*
Went to Dresden yesterday with S. to spend St. Patrick's Day with Frank. A luxurious sanatorium on top of a hill, but such isolation for him! He is undoubtedly seriously ill, and showed me the pulse throbbing visibly in his wrist. A sad day, but better than if we hadn't come.

*March 23rd, 1944. Kreibau.*
A daylight attack and then an alarm at night, so we went to the huge bunker in the Tiergarten where there was considerable confusion, the anti-aircraft ammunition for use by the guns on the top of the tower being carried in at the last minute in coffin-like cases through the main door with the crowd pushing in at the same time.

S. got faint and was given tablets in first-aid room.

Yesterday we came here to stay in a guest house in Silesia for a week or so for a rest from the constant raids.

There was a breakout of British prisoners-of-war from an officers' camp near here and I was stopped and questioned at the railway station. Distraction, heaviness, depression. None of which matters. Goethe wrote in a letter: 'I feel like a rat that has eaten poison and is running from hole to hole.'

The Irish government will not renew my passport. Also, just lately, some threats on the telephone, presumably because I would not give more radio talks.

*March 25, 1944. Kreibau, Silesia.*
We came to this remote, rather primitive gasthaus, run by a friend of a friend of S's, to have a break from the incessant air-raids on Berlin.

Yet the remoteness has no feeling of seclusion. A big, main road outside the door, lorry loads of soldiers passing through the flat Silesian plain with a slight covering of snow. A peculiar desolation!

The Wirtin (landlady) was telling us about an Ukranian maid (one of the forced-labourers from the East) she had been allotted. She was a girl called Sascha whom the landlady had got rid of because, she said, she was dirty. She spoke a little German, learnt at school, and had said one day: "Nicht Geld oder Essen brauch isch, aber mein Ruhe!" (I don't need money or food, just some peace).

Later she got news that her mother and two sisters had been burnt to death in their house in a Russian village.

She cried for days, the Wirtin told us.

*May 1, 1944.*

The last war could be grasped, was personal, had an atmosphere even if it reeked. It was largely fought over a few miles of northern France, around a dozen towns that became almost homely: Ypres, Vimy, Messine Ridge. This conflict nobody can grasp, it is a plague spreading over Russia, over the Pacific, also into every corner. Afterwards there will be no war poetry, no *Goodbye to all That.*

*May 2, 1944.*

More attempts to coerce me back to broadcasting: A letter I wrote to Kay [11] on Good Friday sent back to me marked ABP, Ausland Briefe Politzei, (Foreign Letters Censorship). They have confiscated my passport and I also receive threats over the phone.

They won't arrest me as long as they think there is some chance of my resuming the broadcasts to Ireland, perhaps even agreeing to denounce the "Asian hordes". Luckily, I have some fairly well-placed protectors.

*May 4, 1944.*

This morning was rung up by Weber and later, when I called to the Police Headquarters near the Alexanderplatz, was given my passport (such as it is) back.

A relief! Not that, I think, I was in any great danger.

*Wednesday, May 10, 1944.*

Daylight raids on Sunday and Monday mornings. The Englishche Seminar (English Department at University) hit, my little room there gone and obviously no more work there until the lecture rooms can be repaired.

*August 12, 1944.*
Read of the resignation of Benedetto Croce from the Bonomi
Government. Croce was critical of the Fascist regime in Italy
and is now equally so of the "liberators" and in nether case was
afraid to express his views. Which is the only true liberation.

Some observations on air-raids made last night:

When a two-ton "blockbuster" fell five or six hundred yards
away from where we were in the cellar of this house, we heard
the explosion and felt the place tremble and the electric bulbs
swung slightly on their cables. A couple of seconds later we
heard the sound of the bomb falling, like sand down a chute,
surprisingly clear and lasted three or four seconds. It is *after* the
explosion and ground tremor that what the Germans call the
"Rauschen" is heard, the sound taking longer to travel.

*April 12th, 1945. Southern Germany.*
The horror of crouching (one crouches instinctively though it
would be as well to sit up straight) in a cellar with bombs falling
around, once or twice so close that they throw up a fountain of
earth that we hear as it lands on the roof, the radio announcing
new bomber waves approaching.

Of being without a shelter, of sleeping on station floors, on a
waiting room table edged in with others, when a bed is one of
the great gifts and earthly blessings. Sitting up on a bench all
night, night after night, the head lolling (the foxes have holes
. . . but the son of man has nowhere to lay his head), the cold,
the weariness, the hunger. Hunger is a territory in itself end-
lessly explored with long patches of desert and then the rare
oasis, small and scanty, of a couple of slices of dark bread and
a thin covering of fat. The knowledge that there is nothing else
until next Friday, with another desert in between.

The tiredness by day, the sitting in railway stations and cafés,
waiting, waiting. For what? For the war to end. And then?

The hostility of people like the Liebermans, being partly at
the mercy of those who insult one and resent our very presence.
There is nowhere to go, nowhere to hide. If one goes out there
is the ordeal of coming back, if one leaves a crowded corner
there's the difficulty of finding another one.

*May 8th, 1945. Dornbirn, Vorarlberg.*
The bells are ringing for the official peace on a hot, sunny
evening. We thought the war had ended earlier but evidently

not. There are no papers, sometimes S hears our landlady's radio in the early mornings.

I write at the table in S's tiny room while she has gone up to prepare our supper of gruel. I have put out the two cups and spread the two coloured rags that are our tablecloth.

Shakespeare, Milton and Rilke (whose Elegies we have) sometimes speak words that find an assent in the centre of one's being where very little finds assent. Then I have a conviction and awareness of truth and of having become more responsive to it in these last months.

And in the great world what a lot going on: Hitler dead, Knut Hamsen taken from his home, arrested and harassed, Stalin, victorious, lording it in the Kremlin, Gandhi brooding and fasting in India, the war having passed him by, and all the others, raised up or pulled down.

Reading about the decade or so following the Crucifixion, what a time that was too! In Jerusalem Peter and others of the disciples and rich women sympathisers like Mary the mother of Mark, starting their movement. In Caesarea the Roman Felix making merry and married to a grand-daughter of Anthony and Cleopatra, with Paul in prison in Rome writing his extraordinary Epistles. Agrippa with his golden-haired sister, Berinice, thirsty for sensation, gorgeous and debauched.

We read the Psalms of lamentation and exile, but the old Jews were mostly a stiff-necked people who did not treasure their suffering. So they could not recognise a suffering Messiah.

*May 22nd, 1945.*

The war is over a fortnight, so we, without really knowing it, are that far into the new peace. We've a temporary shelter at last. We rise and go to early Mass celebrated by the French chaplain. We come back to S's tiny room and have breakfast of tea and one slice each of bread and butter (during the coming time rations will be shorter. We still have what was distributed by the shops before the occupation troops marched in). I go into the little town and fetch the milk, anything else that's going and later we read from Eckhart, one of the few books we have. Lunch at noon: a small bowl of *musmehl* (maize porridge), *riepeln* they call it here in Austria, with skimmed milk, some days there is also boiled leeks or spinach.

In the afternoon we sunbathe in the small garden if its sunny or else sleep. Later reading again, Eckhart, the German Missal, Rilke's Elegies. Then perhaps out for a stroll, on the look out for next days vegetables, very hungry again in the warm evening past the gardens of the blackish wooden chalets with their overlapping roofs and deep balconies, mellow and sombre.

Supper at 6.30 with leeks and three or four slices of bread and cheese, with tea, sweet again since we exchanged our cigarette ration for some saccharine.

We say a kind of Vespers, suited to the times and our needs, then talk or read again. It is quiet in the little room, the hours and even quarter hours, chimed by the clock tower in the market square, go very slowly, though below this tranquil surface a strong current is carrying us I don't know where.

Around nine we go to bed in the joy of having one to go to.

**References**

1. Irish Chargé d'Affaires in Berlin from shortly before the war to 1942 when he was succeeded by C.C. Cremin. We became friendly and used to play golf together in the first year or two of the war, when such recreations were still possible.

2. "Liam" is Liam O'Flaherty.

3. Kurt Haller, a member of ABWEHR, had met Frank Ryan at the Spanish frontier and brought him to Berlin, via Paris where they spent a few days, on Ryan's release from Burgos prison in the summer of 1940. I met Haller on several occasions in Berlin during the war, mostly with Frank Ryan or Helmut Clissman. He visited us with Clissman when we lived in Co. Meath around 1963.

4. Cudahy had been United States ambassador in Dublin before the war where I had met him; he had read and liked some of my novels. Later, he became ambassador to Belgium where, after the German occupation, he had entertained officers of the Wehrmacht in the early summer of 1940. Because of this he was either dismissed by Roosevelt or asked to resign. A few weeks later he arrived in Berlin as a political correspondent.

5. A relative, possibly cousin, of Klaus von Stauffenberg who placed the bomb which failed to kill Hitler at his headquarters in July, 1944. He was, when I met him, in charge of the department dealing with prisoners-of-war.

6. Gunther Weissenborn, novelist, later imprisoned by the Nazis, liberated by the Russians in 1945 and, though never a Communist, made Mayor of a town east of Berlin for a short time. When last I heard of him he was living on Lake Constance.

7. My German publisher at the time.

8. Dr. Hans Hartmann, head of broadcasts to Ireland. An Irish-speaker who had spent years in Ireland and is now teaching in a German university.

9. "Frank" is Frank Ryan.

10. "S" — Madeline Stuart, the authors second wife.

11. "Kay" was the novelist's young daughter in Ireland.

# THE DESTROYING ANGEL

When at midday the sirens began to howl on the fluctuating note of gravest warning, Helga felt that, at that moment, everything changed for her. The sky trembled like a curtain that betrays the presence of something lurking behind it. With this trembling of the clear sky all was altered.

When they reached the cellar under the *Pension* this change was accentuated by the sudden coolness of the air, the cellar-smell that became part of these hours. The cellar was narrow, with a bench on each side, and one one of them a doctor and his family, from the ground floor flat, had spread themselves. From the portable wireless that they had brought with them came a tack-tack that was the signal of the station giving the air reports. This monotonous note, like the blows of a minute hammer, repeated in the narrowness of the brightly lit room, became maddening to Louis. The doctor with his family managed to dominate the cellar. The secret of this subtle bullying that he met everywhere never became clear to Louis, nor its counterpart, the passion for submission. He did not know why the owner of the *Pension* and her daughter, with the other lodgers, sat huddled together on one bench speaking in whispers while the doctor's family spread themselves out over the other, eating their sandwiches and fussing with their helmets.

The doctor's voice and his ponderous movements became horrible to Louis in the tension of the narrow crowded cellar. The slow ticking of the wireless stopped and all waited in silence for the announcment. Louis felt the slight trembling of Helga beside him. After the announcement, a whispering broke out from the bench opposite and the doctor took his little boy onto his knees. His wife began to unscrew the top of a thermos flask.

"My God, why don't they keep quiet!" Helga said. "What do you think, are they coming here?" she asked. In his heart he felt they were coming.

"I don't know. They may pass us to the west and go for another city," he said.

"No. They'll come here all right." She knew it too.

"Well, let them come," whispered Louis. He spoke low lest his English be overheard. At the same time he would not speak German although he could do so well enough. He would not speak it, he would speak his own language. He began to try to calculate how many floors they had over them and the thickness of the concrete of the cellar itself.

He knew there was no good in this thinking and calculating, in trusting to thick walls and deep cellars, but he went on with it just the same.

"Listen, little Hare," he said, turning to her. "Our star is more than bombs and bombers."

"What star?" she asked.

"You know what star." He had an instinct against saying more or giving it a name. She looked at him to see whether he really believed in this star now, at such an hour.

"We don't submit to the terror of any of their machines," he said, "because no machine can destroy us in our star."

The doctor's family began putting on their helmets, led by the ponderous figure of the doctor himself. They took their time from him, doing all with a deliberation that was unbearable to Louis.

The Terror-by-Day was creeping up the sky towards them, and frightful was this waiting in the bright little cellar to the soft hammer blows of the wireless signal. But even at these moments Louis knew that this was not the worst of the war-horror; this was the explosive fury of the machine outside them, and it was easier to remain unsubmitted to it than to the slow grinding of the machine day in, day out stamping the very details of their existence with its image. Yet even so that they were not submitted, and, as he had told her, the final horror had not come, the machine had not yet been able to grind its way into their hidden kingdom; it was not yet the Abomination of Desolation sitting in the holy place.

When the attack burst over them the cellar filled with a pandemonium of noise. But it was not the loudest noises that were the most deadly. What crept into the marrow of their bones were the tremors that ran through the concrete, passing from wall to wall. The worst terror was in these tremors and in a whisper that came out of the air. It was in the low rushing sound, like the sound of sand filling down a shute; that was the whisper of the wings of the destroying angel, he thought, this soft noise of the bombs as they fell. And when it was heard in the cellar all bowed themselves over their knees.

The attack grew louder, bursting into a ghastliness of noise. The world was exploding around them; only within them was a frail little non-explosive core. Everywhere else the cracking apart of the world in explosions. This passed, and there was only left a kind of rocking of the earth, heavy and sodden, and the air in the cellar filling with the smell of dust and earth.

"That was the house falling," Helga whispered.

"It was like the heavens falling," Louis said.

A voice came from the doctor's wireless, that was to Louis a diabolical little instrument of torment, announcing the approach of the second wave of bombers. Helga was shuddering in long deep shudders as the earth had shuddered, and when he spoke to her, trying to comfort her, she did not look at him.

"It will go over, little Hare, it will pass over."

She sat with her head bowed, convulsed in shudders that came from her very soul, over which the shadow of the destroying angel had passed.

"Let me be," she whispered, "let me only keep still."

"Like a real hare," he said to her, "that hears the hunters."

If they were saved out of this, if they were brought back again to the flow of life in days and nights, he would know the sweetness of each hour of quietness by her side. His heart could never again harden against her. All hardness of heart would melt in the sweetness of being beside her in quietness. To walk along a street with her in the quiet of an afternoon with the evening and the long, still night before them! Now what they had before them was the second wave of the attack.

It began like all the others, with a distant murmur and then the sound of the bombers passing overhead. Louis could feel them overhead, slowly passing, and beside him Helga bowed within the circle of his arm. The second wave went over and the bombers were reported to be on their homeward flight.

Louis took his arm from around her and stretched and

looked about the small, dust-filled cellar. There was something in his coming back to life that was like the coming-to out of the shuddering trance of sleeping together.

There was a stir in the cellar as the doctor's family took off their helmets and folded up their rugs. Louis picked up his attaché case in which were his drawings and the rest of their few valuables.

"Let's wait a little," she said. "There is no hurry."

He was glad to put the case down again and wait beside her. Now he felt the plenitude of time being given back to them, being poured like balm into their bosom. But when the others, except for the two old ladies who remained nodding their heads and whispering on their bench, had filed through the door, they, too, got up.

In their rooms the hand of destruction had not made one sweep, but a series of almost delicate movements, leaving a vase and jug standing on the table but tearing the doors from their hinges and strewing earth over the beds. A smell of smoke, bitter and reminding them of the previous autumn in Berlin when for days they had lived with this taste in their noses and mouths, came through the gaping windows. The sunshine was gone and all was darkened by a pile of smoke clouds, drifting across the sky.

Helga found a brush, tied up her hair in a cloth, and began sweeping up the earth and fragments of glass. This business of cleaning up was the beginning of life for her again, her emergence out of the shadow. But, in the middle of it, she put the broom aside and they lay down together on the dusty bed in the darkened room. She lay shuddering in his arms and was afterwards still, as though it had required this to drive the last shadow of horror out of her.

Afterwards they went out to inspect the havoc. A stream of people, carrying their salvaged belongings, were moving down the wide poplar avenue under the yellowish, grey sky. Louis and Helga mingled with another crowd out to view the smoking ruins. They saw two new bomb craters in the wide avenue opposite the *Pension* and there was a carpet of green leaves across the street from the nearest poplars that had been stripped naked by the blast. They began to search for the traces of other bombs nearby, drawn to the fresh craters, standing beside them, almost brooding over them as though entranced. A bomb had fallen onto a house in a narrow street behind the *Pension,* and as they came up a body was being carried out of the débris on a door by four soldiers. It was a long bundle of rags covered in dust, and it was slid off the door into a lorry backed up on to the pavement to receive it. They could not see into the lorry but they went on staring at it, as did the others in the small crowd.

But then they walked away. In the end they had felt that it was shameless, this staring at the bodies of the dead, feeding on the sight of their stillness, of their dustiness. At the corner they passed a cinema about to begin its afternoon performance. Helga hesitated, looking at the bright poster.

"Shouldn't we go?" she asked, appealing to him.

"That's a stupid film," he said, "and we've still our rooms to put in order, and later there will be no light."

"I don't mind; let it be stupid," she said, "our rooms can wait. Now I want to see fine dresses and kisses."

Dresses and kisses were the farthest in one direction she could get from where they had been.

"My God, come on then," he said. He would go with her wherever she wanted. Inside, sitting together int he half-dark, she took his hand and whispered: "Don't despise me. Here it's so cosy!"

When they came out night had fallen over the burning city and the sky glowed a muddy pink. At home they lit a candle that Helga had brought with her from Berlin. Because of the fires the back-out regulations had been lifted and they saw the little squares of glass still left in the patched up windows around them flickering with candle light. They ate their supper of bread and *Wurst* and drank their beer, and all was good with the blessed taste of life.

"What were you thinking of in the cellar as you sat there bowed and trembling?" he asked her.

"I listen," she said, "that is all I do really; listen and tremble! But you, you can pray."

"Hardly at all."

"Once when I looked at you and thought: what strength he has! And that can only come from praying. But when I begin to pray I think: there is no good praying, there are thousands and thousands praying for the same thing and to all of them it won't be given."

"One can't pray not to be killed," he said, "but one can pray for something else. I'm not sure what it is that I pray about, but it is not that we should not be killed."

Next morning they were out early, hunting for bread that was always difficult to get after a raid. The sunlight had begun to filter through the veil of smoke. They had come through the porch of death out into this unexpected new intensity of shared peace. They walked the streets through the thick dust into which all was being reduced. Never before had Louis felt the sweet intensity of living; the miracle of life. In the white Australian days he had moved thinly, ghost-like and half-extinguished compared to this. They went on towards the centre of the town, towards the cathedral, climbing over hills of bricks with which many of the streets were blocked. They did not wait in any of the queues. They felt withdrawn, alone together in their fiery cloud and they did not want to begin just yet the business of waiting, of calculating whether anything would be left when their turn came. They walked on towards the Frauenkirche.

"If only it hasn't been hit!" Louis said. He thought that he did not really mind what had been hit except for this cathedral.

"But that will go sooner or later too; all will be destroyed in the end," Helga said.

"Well, let it. We can't stop it; we can only let it go on," Louis answered, "let the wind of destruction blow everything to dust as long as we and a few others are at the same time being kindled to intenser life. It's what happens to those still left, not what happens to the cities, that matters. Unless there are a few people like us in all the countries who have begun to tend their own shining life within themselves, turned away from the machine, there won't be any peace afterwards. Peace can't just be created by the signing of a document; that may stop the havoc, but it won't make anything grow out of the dust. The seed of the tree of life must be sown there, and this seed must be treasured somewhere now, in a few people."

So he talked as they came out onto the Frauenplatz and she listened and believed him. And there was the cathedral looming over them like a smooth, towering rock. They walked round it, under its huge sides. Only in front, near the great arch of the door, there were a few pale chips in the dark red bricks. They went inside and sat down by the altar of the Black Virgin. To Louis this black virgin on the pedestal, dim between the shadows of the pillars, with her gleaming crown, was powerless. With her bitter little face and the stiff folds of her garments she was no match for the destroying angel that was lord of the night outside. And the whole cathedral in its dim stone-beauty was no match for it; and it was like a bloom loose on its stalk. For all its rock-like looming and its great vaulted arches it was over-blown and would not stand against the breath of the destroying angel.

He saw that there was no good weeping over the doomed cathedral; better they gather themselves into the beam of their star that was inviolate, constant. They must let the cathedral go; they must let all go if needs be and not waste their tears. This great dim, stone prayer-machine would be destroyed by another machine and blown away into the dust. But underground, in the underground of their spirits, and of others too, a new sap was flowing, beginning to kindle new buds, that were hard and tight on the stalk and would not be swept away!

# EXTRACTS FROM
# THE JOURNAL OF AN APATRIATE

*Aug. 10, 1945:* At last, with the series of jolts that I was now accustomed to, the train moved slowly into the Gare de l'Est. There was some more delay and an air of uncertainty as the repatriates stood around in the station with their luggage and two French women in uniform did not seem to know what to do with us. A young man with painted finger nails strolled up and taking charge of the weary travellers, herded us into some ancient green buses. Thus we came to the rue Leonardo da Vinci off the Place Victor Hugo. Here in this narrow, fashionable street several large houses had been converted into reception camps by simply filling their rooms, whose ceilings were richly moulded and whose doors were elaborately panelled, with rows of the usual double-tiered beds.

*Aug. 11:* The first proper meal for three years: Meat stewed in red sauce, and a pile of macaroni. While a little Jewess next to me began scraping the sauce from her portion of meat and examining it suspiciously, I devoured my helping and swallowed a tin mugful of red wine. Each meal now seems better than the previous one, and it strikes me that there is nothing like eating a piece of meat in just this strong reddish sauce and washing it down with a long draught of Algerian wine.

After lunch wandered through the house until I found a room in which were basins and a mirror. The filth of the basins and the fact that the floor of the room was under water did not bother me. When I felt I was sufficiently clean to appear at the consulate, I went to the Yugoslav who sat at the table in the portico and asked him where this was. He spoke in German, the common language of the camp, lazily turning over the leaves of a telephone directory. With his other hand he felt in the drawer of the table, and, bringing out a packet of Gauloises, tossed them to me. This gesture, more than the wooden buckets of wine, more than the pieces of fat lying under the tables, brought it home to me that the seven lean years were at least temporarily over.

When I arrived at the porter's lodge of the consulate I was told that I was too late, the reception hours ending at four. In my meagre French I tried to express an opinion that, as one of the few nationals of this particular country who had been lost and was returning, as it were, to the fold, as a wanderer miraculously appearing out of the wilderness, I was not subject to these petty regulations, and that I wished to have my arrival announced. But the French porter neither followed nor wished to follow the language of this disreputable looking visitor.

*Aug. 12:* Walked along the avenue Victor Hugo to the Place d'Etoile. Stood there at the edge of the stream of traffic circling round the great grey rock of the Arc de Triomphe. This was the great world, and watching it, the cars and the people in them, I felt a deep distate of it. Here at last was civilised life again and I felt a complete stranger in the midst of it.

At ten, again presented myself before the porter of the consulate, and after some time in a waiting-room was called by the consul into his office. The first thing that I noticed, after the consul himself, was his black hat with an elegant curl to its brim, hanging on a coat-strand in a corner. This fascinated me more than anything I had yet seen. Imagined him putting it on and getting into his black car and charging around the great rock of the Arc de Triomphe. If he turns out to be civil it will be no harm to have him as an ally in the great, roaring world through which I must pass. Said he would have my case looked into and I am to return this afternoon.

*Later:* "You were not interned, Mr. X?" the consul asked me after another long wait in ante-room.

"No. Were you?"

"I shall send a cable about the renewal of your passport but, taking all the circumstances into consideration, I am very doubtful about attaining any positive result."

"How long will that take?"

"Two or three weeks."

"And what am I to live on meanwhile?"

"You have a bank-account at home, I suppose?"

"No."

"There you are. In that case your predicament is a very equivocal one. I would not care to take the responsibility of advising you."

"A thousand thanks."

*Aug. 14: Notes on the Camp:* This is officially run by an effeminate young sergeant who has a room at the top of the house from which he occasionally emerges in beautifully creased uniform trousers and sandals, and pads ineffectually around the drier parts of the building. Most of his work seems to be done by his German girl who, now that the leaves of the big chestnut tree are beginning to turn, queens it in a white rabbit-skin jacket among the shabbily dressed repatriates. She is known as Marcel's girl and, at first, I had been somewhat in awe of her and her mysterious functions, but as I get to know her I find her kind and helpful. The house is really run however by the big Yugoslav with thick wavy hair and a wrinkled, weather-beaten face. It was to him that I spoke yesterday about the possibility of getting a room in a hotel and continuing to eat at the camp (having the day before received the sum of four thousand francs from the consul). To the Yugoslav there was no difficulty at all in the arrangement. Once I had a room he told me I could have my meals in a house just round the corner in the rue Lerroux. (The bugs that infested the camp made this more advisable.)

"You've only got to say a word to Jules and give him a cigarette now and then."

The house in the rue Lerroux is larger and more palatial than that in the rue Leonardo da Vinci. In the upper parts various officers of the *Centre de Repartriment* have luxurious bureaux and in the basement the repatriates eat and the food for the camps in the houses is prepared. It was there I found the little Belgian, Jules, with a round face, and, behind thick glasses, pale eyes perpetually screwed up against the smoke of the cigarette that was always in his mouth. He was presiding over a group of seven or eight repatriates who had just sat down to lunch.

"From the rue Leonardo da Vinci?" repeated Jules, pretending to look into a grubby note-book. I offered him a cigarette, the one hanging from his lip having burnt down to the last few threads of tobacco, and, when he took it, told him to keep the rest of the packet.

"Yes, that's all right," Jules said out of the free corner of his mouth. Sat down at the table, and before the meal was over found that the dark little fellow next me was a Russian who had been educated at an English Public School and still spoke with an Eton accent. His name was Darykov and he was a refugee in Paris with his Hungarian wife. He spoke of a residence in Cyprus, of British papers which had been cancelled, of children boarded out at a Salvation army hostel and of all the other eternal complications that were the habitual lot of us apatriates.

*Aug. 12:* Went yesterday, on Darykov's advice, with him to the Peruvian Consulate, where, he had been told, it was possible to obtain a visa on our Repatriation cards in return for agreeing to work two years as agricultural labourers in a part of Peru which, he assured me, was extremely salubrious. After two hours in queue, nothing came of this.

"You've got to keep worrying them," Darykov tells me twice a day. He brings new addresses at which to apply. I put the slips of paper into my pocket with the others and do not try to explain my apparent lethargy. I have never believed in trying to force things. The great events come in their own way and time, for me, anyhow. I change the subject, nodding at the rows of inscriptions on the bell indicator: Salle de bain de M. le Baron, boudoir de Mme. la Baronne. I say, for instance: "Who the devil was M. le Baron, I wonder?"

"Oh, that! Probably the Baron de Rothschild. But have you been over to number sixty, avenue Foch? That's where the headquarters of the Ministry for Repartriés et déportés are."

*Aug. 20:* No news. It seems the only thing left is for me to return whence I came. But don't know how to set about this.

*Aug. 21:* Consulted the Yugoslav.

"Yes, it is possible," he told me. "All is possible, if you go about it in the right manner."

(By now I have begun to see that my immediate future is to consist in learning to be an apatriate among apatriates, and any clinging to the idea of being anything else, a writer, for instance, is a useless struggle against the flow of destiny.)

He paused to hear what an apatriate who had been waiting in the background wanted.

"Bugs!" he said. "I know damn well there are bugs here. But I can't conjure them away, can I? I'm not a bleeding magician.

That's Marcel's business, why don't you go and complain to him, eh?"

"Where is he?" asked the little Bulgarian professor timidly.

"He's where he always is — in bed with that German whore of his." He turned back to me.

"You go and speak to Mademoiselle sous-Lietenant Courcelles over in the house where you feed. Tell her to put your name down for the next transport. Only you've got to get hold of her in the mornings; she spends her afternoons with American sergeants. But at least she has picked up some English from them so that you can talk to her in your own lingo."

*Aug. 21:* Found Mademoiselle Courcelles in her office. A tall girl with a mass of fair, reddish hair and a pretty, freckled face. She spoke English that she had certainly picked up from no United States sergeants, but had probably learnt in some expensive academy for girls.

"You're no sooner free than half of you are wanting to go back," she said. "I must go and have a talk with the Americans about you. Come around again early next week, will you, please? I shall put you on the list."

Went away with a certain faith in the young sous-lieutenant and her list. That such a list existed, that was already something.

*Aug. 25:* "I've had an awful lot of trouble over you," the Mademoiselle sous-Lieutanant Courcelles told me. "I don't mean only over you, but over all who want to go back."

"The thing is, can we go back?"

"I think so. I've got you on to a transport, only you're German, you understand; you can speak some German, can't you, if anyone asks? You had better be in the rue Leonardo da Vinci tomorrow evening with your luggage at six o'clock."

"I think there is a possiblity of getting to Germany in a few days," I told Darykov later. I was proud of being on the list, any list was better than none, better than being completely disowned.

"But it's Austria you want to go to, old fellow, isn't it?"

*Aug. 26:* Yesterday evening, as promised, a bus drove up to the camp and an American lieutant got out and was presented by Mademouseille Courcelles with the list. When our little group had climbed in he read out our names and we were driven to the

Gare de l'Est. At the station the lieutenant shepherded us to a corner near the barrier, and told us to wait until he returned.

" They will send me to Hungary," a Hungarian boy said to me anxiously. "That's what will happen to me. They will send me home."

"You don't want to go?"

He shook his head.

"Why do you go then? You're not a prisoner?"

Bewilderment on the part of the boy. "I don't know, but I cannot go back," he repeated.

"Well, don't go back. There is the exit to the street over there. Take your rucksack and walk through it."

The boy hesitated a moment and then took up his luggage and walked quickly away through the crowd.

"Where's he gone? Dr. Bogusky, who was in charge of the party, asked.

"He's gone away."

The Latvian took the list out of his pocket and I looked at it over his shoulder. The sheet was headed: "To the United States officer in charge, Chalons-sur-Marne" and was a request that those on it should be repatriated to the places indicated against their names. Against my name was that of a town I could not decipher.

*Aug. 27:* Arrival in Chalons-sur-Marne. Started out with Dr. Bogusky to look for the American officer.

Rain was falling as we made our way across a wooden bridge over the river and along a muddy road into the town. Each time we were splashed by the American lorries and jeeps jolting by over the filled-up bomb-craters, Dr. Bogusky stopped and carefully wiped the drops from the ends of his grey trousers.

Arrived at a house in a dreary square from whose porch the French and American flags hung limply in the rain. Entered a room whose door was labelled "Colonel so-and-so" in which, of course, there was no colonel but a couple of women, smoking cigarettes and occasionally moving from typewriter to telephone with the high-heeled French walk.

Again the showing of papers, the flow of French and the sinking of heart.

Watched closely the Latvian as he folded up his papers again, but his thin face was impassive and from the conversation itself I had gathered that nothing could be done until the colonel came in the afternoon. The rain had increased to a downpour and we waited in the hall for it to abate while the doctor told me that the French women advised us to apply to the Displaced Persons' Camp in another part of the town.

Took advantage of the delay to go to the lavatory and clean myself up, not having had an opportunity to wash since Paris. There was a big square of yellow soap on the wash-basin that gave off a foamy lather, a sign of the presence of the Americans more impressive than the limp stars-and-stripes drooping from its staff over the porch. Wrapped the big hunk of soap in a piece of paper and put it in my pocket.

At the office of the Displaced Persons' Camp we were received by yet another girl in uniform, who after a short talk with Bogusky pushed a large book towards him, in which she asked him to sign our names.

"She says we must stay here two or three days while a *laissez-passer* over the frontier is being made out for us," the doctor said.

*Sept. 4:* After a fruitless week of waiting, escaped from the camp in Chalons-sur-Marne and continued the journey with the remnants of group, to Strasbourg.

Here we were directed to the *Deuxième Bureau,* the office of the French military intelligence, and, while the others waited in the background, Doctor Bogusky and myself went up to the table of an elderly little colonel.

The doctor began his explanation and unfolded his two papers which the officer read. He turned to his adjutant at another table and referred the case to him.

"It is a matter for the Prefect of Police," said the adjutant. "Ring up the Prefect and tell him we are sending Doctor Bogusky over to him. It's a special case." The colonel glanced again at the doctor's papers. "Doctor Bogusky was of great service, while in charge of the refugee camp at Lagenau, to the French Republic."

I listened with astonishment. With such a document in his pocket I no longer wondered at the doctor's air of cool superiority. My heart sank as I made my own request to the shiny, pink-cheeked face; I had been of no service to anything and had nothing to show but an invalid passport. The colonel waved me to the table of the adjutant who was ringing up the Police Prefecture.

*Sept. 5:* The doctor and I were interviewed by the Prefect, the others sent to another room. Was told my application would be considered and to return in three days. What the doctor was told did not discover, the Latvian preserving a superior silence, on account, no doubt, of his excellent paper. The others had disappeared into one of the many office of the big building.

*Sept. 7:* On going back to the Prefecture no trace of application could be found and was told to wait another couple of days. My French not being good enough to explain prolonged stay in the *repatriement hut* impossible, was interviewed by a young woman who spoke English, specially called in. She suggested I should come back with her to the Prefecture, where she herself worked, and she would try to trace application.

*Sept. 9:* No trace of application. No possiblity of staying on in Strasbourg. Return to Paris in company of an apatriate of Polish origin.

*Sept. 10:* Return of the raven to the Ark. No branch, nothing. The sous-lieutenant listend sympathetically.

"Come round from time to time. The Americans have a way of doing things when least expected."

Melkowsky asked that his name should be added to the new list.

"You want to go to Poland?"

"To Germany, my dear lady."

"En route for Poland?"

"Certainly."

*Sept. 20:* Yesterday a new transport was suddenly reported to be leaving. This time under more propitious auspices. The young sergeant was wandering around in his sandals and beautifully pressed trousers with his German girl, in her white rabbit-skin jacket, hanging on his arm. She told me that this time she was going too.

"And Marcel is coming with us as far as the frontier to see that there is no trouble."

At supper Melkowsky shuffled in late and brought some rumour that the transport had been postponed.

"Nonsense, I was talking to Mademoiselle Courcelles an hour ago," an apatriate next to him said. There was a general nervousness among those going on the transport.

"All right, my dear lady, we shall see," muttered Melkow-sky, bent over his plate of beans. He alone seemed indifferent as to whether it went or not.

Disliked Melkowsky at that moment with his jacket smeared with soap and his whole indifferent air, noisily eating his beans and scowling to himself. But a few moments later, Mademoiselle Courcelles appeared with the typed list in her hand.

*Sept. 21:* At Metz we waited on the platform while Marcel went off to enquire about some goods trains to which we were to be attched. Saw a fatal similarity with the arrival at Strasbourg. After a long delay Marcel came back and began talking to his girl in a low voice while a little group of apatriates gathered anxiously around him. Girl's raised voice protesting angrily that she refused to go to any camp.

"Only for to-night," Marcel said, "you are going on to-morrow morning."

"I know that tomorrow morning of yours. I'm not going to leave this platform."

Marcel looked round helplessly, and began to explain to the others that he had been able to find out nothing about any east bound goods train. In the end a despondent move was made towards the station exit. Marcel, with his girl dragging reluctantly on his arm, followed in the rear. Outside the station the luggage was again piled up and the little crowd stood forlornly around. A lorry backed up to the pavement and its tail-board was let down. We were driven through the town and beyond it across a bridge over the Moselle. Beside the river rose a gaunt barracks built in the shape of a square, and through a gate-way in this the lorry drove and the heavy doors were shut behind it. When the little group of apatriates climbed out we found ourselves in an arch-way under one of the blocks separated from the big inner square by a barbed wire gate through which a ragged-looking crowd was watching our arrival. The sight of the barbed wire and the look of those beyond it, confirmed our forebodings. Flight of Marcel and girl, leaving us to our fate.

*Oct. 22:* Yesterday, after three weeks in the desolate barracks, we were herded to a platform at the goods station where a long line of cattle trucks were awaiting us. Settled myself in the corner of a waggon. It was cold in the night and in the morning we had only reached Strasbourg, where, in a net-work of lines somewhere outside the station, there was another interminable delay. A girl came along from truck to truck distributiing American Red Cross parcels. Snow had fallen in the night and covered the expanse of tracks. The Yugoslavs climbed down and lit fires beside the train, boiling coffee and heating the various tins from the American packets.

Jumped down and stood between the tracks by a big fire. The American captain in charge of the transport, who had been drunk the night before, emerged from the passenger carriage at the end of the train in which he had his quarters. He agreed that the fact that in over twelve hours we had only travelled from Metz to Strasbourg was very discouraging. He was a small, thick-set American with humorous eyes and he stood there in his military overcoat shivering and sending members of his little staff to enquire what was happening.

Climbed back into waggon where Melkowsky was finishing up his share of the rations that were meant to last the whole day. Sat on the straw and ate a tin of sardines and then the contents of a tin of jam for which I had no more biscuits left. to go with."

"Looks like being an early winter," says Melkowsky.

"Early or late, damn all odds it makes to us. As we do not know where we shall spend it, with whom, or under what conditions, there is no point in worrying over the weather. Worry can only begin when there is some minimum of plan or expectation."

# JACOB

A word about Jacob MacGregor's background and present circumstances. It's enough, without delving into personal history, to record that this man with the blanched face evidently in the grip of an intense obsession is a widower with a son at school (his third in the course of the year) and a training establishment at the Curragh to which he moved some years previously from the larger family one.

At the break-up of the household there had been grief and bitterness, pain and resentment. No need to go into that. There are traces both of Semetic and gypsy blood in him which make it hard to take such things easily. (A Jewish grandfather put the Celtic prefix before the family name of Gregor and he came to Ireland to train horses).

Jacob took with him to his new quarters, the head lad, Corcoran; and to deepen the rift between himself and his wife, the stable jockey, Matt Macey, came and offered him first call on his services the day after the move.

Those are old patterns, faded and bleached in the glare of the pressing present moments in the story. On this latest of which he had come to town and was staying at the hotel owned by a patron of his, Manzini, and had gone out to eat at a restaurant in the same ownership.

Two things went on in his mind, both urgent and, as usual, confusing in their apparently opposite compulsions. One was the lift-girl who'd taken him up to his room at his arrival an hour ago, and the other was the thought of his favourite dish that he had come here to order. While awaiting being served he sat with his face, that felt too big and exposed at moments of crisis, half covered by one of his hands.

He was shading his eyes, shutting out the rest of the room

and trying to have another look at her. Dark. Fragile build. Plain, gold ear-rings. None of this was to the point. Long legs in jeans, simple, white blouse. Equally irrelevant.

What was it that had so disturbed and excited him? (why were they taking all evening over his order?); the faint luminosity on her brow, grave, lucid, a reflection of the torch of God (his vocabulary, though restricted, was capable of poetry).

At last the *Porchetta veritabile Romana* which he could only get in this restaurant (though his housekeeper Katie Muldoon could make a fair attempt at it when in the mood) was placed before him.

With the flies buzzing round the small table, he ate and ate, filling his mouth with crackling morsels of sucking-pig roasted to a deep bronze and flavoured with garlic and something that he imagined as mandrake (or mandragora root), and washing them down with gulps of the raw Frascati wine.

He felt better, less agitated, more relaxed. That, of course, was a manner of speaking, a short-cut through complex emotions. It did not mean that he wasn't still under the spell of the lift-girl. Her effect on him had been spiritual and sensual at the same time. That was always the trouble with Jacob; he was susceptible to all kinds of conflicting urges. He had an impulse to kneel before her, touch his big mouth to the end of her blue jeans and, on the other hand, if he let himself go, he could imagine, when alone in the lift with her, trying to slip his hand down the front of her blouse.

Soon the heat, the flies (not that it was a cheap joint, far from it), the letters from his son, Joseph, burning in an inside pocket, the Italian wine (at twelve shillings the litre), were combining to produce in him a nervous state of anxious expectation. Manzini (he dropped in for an hour or two each evening to keep an eye on things) came to the table to welcome Jacob whom he'd missed when he arrived at the hotel. Before Manzini could ask about the two-year-old he was training for him, Jacob got in first with his question.

"What girl, Mr. MacGregor?"

He leant towards Jacob, his sallow face thrust right across the small table, waiting, to be told about the colt and not really having heard what he'd been asked.

"The elevator-operator."

"That's my daughter, Mr. MacGregor. A very shy girl."

"I thought I noticed a resemblance," Jacob lied to explain his curiosity.

"You did? Nobody ever said that before. She's a difficult kid, Mr. MacGregor. She keeps her sign permanently at 'stop', never lets it change to 'wait' or 'go'. Not like my other girl behind the reception desk."

Two daughters, both working in the hotel; but Jacob wasn't to be deflected by the father's rather blatant mention of the second. With Manzini there was always a degree of crudity. This also applied to his questions about Johnny. Jacob had to try to indicate to him some of the subtleties and uncertainties involved in running a two-year old in only his second race.

"There are colts (I've seldom known it to happen with fillies) who slumber the best part of their first season away. That's how it's been with our fellow, he wasn't fully awake in his only race. It wasn't until the last couple of furlongs that he began to get the hang of what was going on. Matt Macey could tell the exact moment he woke up under him."

Manzini was hanging on every word, bewildered, suspicious and hopeful.

"You reckon he is wide awake now?"

"That's something I'll be able to tell when I saddle him in his box tomorrow."

"You must have some idea as to how he'll run, that's all I'm asking."

Manzini was breathing right across the table, his black eyes on Jacob as if to try to detect what he thought was wilfully being withheld from him.

Next morning Jacob was up early reckoning, correctly, that it was his best chance of being alone in the lift with Miss Manzini. He had noted her slight limp and used it as an excuse to start a more intimate conversation than one on the weather.

"I'm not a doctor but I know something about muscular trouble."

"It's not muscular."

Did she think it strange how often he went to his room and came down again in the course of the morning? But she didn't as much as smile when the door slid open and there he was again. They were not always alone, and it was during the fifth or sixth ascent and descent before he got her to tell him that she suffered from the effects of a car crash a year or so before in which her mother had been killed.

There was no one waiting for the elevator in the hall on that occasion and, still talking, she pressed the button that closed the door and took him up with her again.

After her physical injuries had healed she was left with an intermittent humming or buzzing in her head. She only heard it lying down and, at first, she had thought the sound came from under the pillow.

"They had told me at the hospital that the noises were caused by a nervous condition which would clear up in the course of time, but they were becoming more insistent."

Later that morning when Jacob was driving Manzini to the course the latter announced:

"I'm afraid it's bad news, Mr. MacGregor."

Jacob, with thoughts now on the coming race, had supposed that whatever news there was (he'd been talking to his head lad, Corcoran, on the phone) would come from him.

"I mean about my little girl. I should have told you last night, she's more or less of an invalid, suffers from some nervous trouble. But my elder daughter, you haven't met her yet, she's another story altogether. I'll introduce you to her this evening."

"Oh, I was only . . . "

Manzini interrupted: "Don't let it bother you. When we get back to town tonight you can take Lucy out, she's a little *Nectarino,* and you won't give another thought to Pieta. That's a promise, Mr. MacGregor."

This sort of talk embarrassed Jacob. The last words struck him as especially crude, as if he was being offered the elder girl as some sort of incentive or reward.

The rain that had been falling all morning increased as they drove towards the course. Jacob was keeping an eye out for a break in the clouds. The softer the ground the greater the test for the little colt whom he hadn't yet managed to put the work into that would have left him hard and fit. But with the stands and racecourse buildings loomed up it was in a wet glimmer against a dark curtain of rain.

He dropped Manzini at the entrance to the course and, after parking the car, went to the stables. Corcoran was sitting on a pile of straw in a corner of Johnny's box, his back to the wall, with a folded sheet of newspaper on his drawn-up knees which he was pretending to read in the dim light coming in over the open to half of the door. He made a move to get up, but Jacob told him to stay where he was.

"How's everything!"

"Middling, Mr. MacGregor."

Corcoran's eyes under the low brim of the hat he wore in all weather, indoors and out, were neither on his master nor the sheet of newspaper but had never left a spot on the flat of the colt's neck.

Jacob knew he liked to preserve an atmosphere of melancholy before a race on which much depended, seeming to believe that, being lived through beforehand, the way was left clearer for a happy outcome.

The rain gurgling in a down pipe from a gutter over the stable door increased the sense of anxiety.

Jacob ran a hand along Johnny's flank and the skin flowed along under his palm and then slipped back in its own strong counter-current. The horse was beginning to sense that something was going to be asked of him but hadn't been before.

Drip . . . gurgle . . . drip. A clatter of hooves on brick, a rattle of buckets and, from the distance, the first eerie notes as the bookies from under their wide umbrellas started calling the odds on the first race. Johnny raised his bony head with the pale star aglimmer at the top of the narrow front, and Corcoran gave a murmur.

"What's that?" Jacob asked anxiously.

"Just telling him there's nothing to worry about. You're not going to advise the owner to back him, Mr. MacGregor?"

"I don't know yet."

"There's a couple of animals in the race whose connections don't care what happens to them as long as they land the money today."

Corcoran had been talking to the other travelling lads.

Jacob didn't go to look for Manzini when he got to the course. He moved around with the idea that he might hear or notice something that would give him some idea of the strength of the opposition in the two-year-old event. Though he knew that this was a vain hope. Those trainers with likely runners in the same race seemed to avoid him with a perfunctory "Afternoon, MacGregor," or a passing: "How-are-you, Jamie" (he was called James or Jamie by most of his colleagues). Though by now he was to tense that he might be imagining all this.

He took a look at the horses parading for the first race and then at the bookmakers' boards which, however, didn't yct concern him. He was drawn several times to the far end of the grand stand to peer out in the direction from which the clouds were coming.

He saw to it that he didn't meet Manzini until shortly before the race in which Johnny was running when he was waiting in the centre of the parade ring, which on these occasions has something about it of a church ceremonial, a wedding or a procession in honour of a saint, with the jockeys decked out in their silks, the burnished colts and fillies placing their hooves with pious delicacy on the gravelly aisle as they're led round.

But this bit of formal pageantry always made Jacob doubly aware of the foam-flecked, sweaty consummation in which all was going to end. He suffered from pre-race nerves to a degree that nobody would have guessed from what he thought of as his coarse-grained exterior.

Matt Macey came up in Manzini's brown and silver hoops, brown sleeves, and touched his cap with the perfunctory gesture of a jockey who knows that from now on all is in his hands.

"Keep him up handy with the leaders if I can, sir, and smack him one if I have to when it comes to it?" Macey asked from out of the side of his mouth away from the colt's owner.

"Right. Except that you don't touch him with the whip, Matt."

"And if it comes to a tight finish?" Manzini enquired.

The jockey's face remained blank, a yellowish mask the texture of dried apple-skin. He took in nothing at these moments except the few words Jacob spoke in a certain low tone that got throught he shutter he'd pulled down. What Manzini or anybody else said didn't touch him. He stood between trainer and owner, bow-legged in his white breeches, arms akimbo, head on one side (a bright-plumaged bird about to take off) quite motionless but for a twitch of the whip that sprouted from under his left elbow.

After Jacob had given him a leg up he went with Manzini to the rails where the bookmakers stood.

Hey, what was this? Manzini was thrusting a bundle of

Jacob

notes, five and ten-pound ones, into his hands.

"Put these on with your own."

This wasn't the right sign at all. What Jacob had been hoping for was the recollection of some small incident not fully grasped at the time, from the training grounds, that he could suddenly interpret in a way that would clear up the uncertainty.

"No, you haven't given me much encouragement, Mr. Mac Gregor. But I know it's not your way. I heard what you told the jockey and that's enough."

Jacob took the notes and put them into his pocket. Then, in a low tone, he made their combined bet on credit with a bookie whom he knew. Immediately all along the line of blackboards the odds against Johnny's name were rubbed out. Without waiting to see what price was being substituted he followed Manzini onto the part of the stand marked: "owners and trainers only."

Races, for those deeply involved, tend to divide up into three acts, each of about twenty seconds (if it's a five-furlong affair) on the electric clock. (A timing that has no correspondence to the duration as measured on the inner chronometer.)

In the first of these phases covering, say, two furlongs, and still far-removed even through binoculars, there's a feeling of relief, even of leisureness, after the tension of the preliminaries. So it was now. For those fleeting seconds Jacob could have been a distant spectator of some colourful and unhurried display on a summer afternoon. Except that he still had had, right up to the "off", one eye on the clouds. Though another shower couldn't make any difference to the going, this sudden darkening of the scene added to the feeling that all judgement based on knowledge of the colt's capabilities and a study of the form of the other runners was having its last frail validity washed away out there behind the rain-mist.

Then came the second phase when names are strung out by the race commentator like the words of a litany, some repeated, some soon discarded,while through the curtain of rain and a momentary gap in the oncoming wall, he saw the silver and brown hoops, silver cap.

"Holy Mother, where is he?"

Only Manzini muttering in his sleep. Of which no notice need be taken. Phase three began as soon as Jacob could make out Macey nestled down on Johnny in the middle of the field, no doubt catching through hands and knees the imtimations coming from the colt, and with the corners of his eyes registering signs and portents from the runners nearest him.

"Mamma mia, is he going to be beaten?"

"Just a moment, Manzini."

This was the vital test when Matt Macey was conveying to his mount that, far from it being time to relax his pull on the bit and take a breather, that the moment of moments had come (as it hadn't in his only other race) to drop the head lower and extend the swing of forelegs a few extra inches.

Now, too, was the moment when, for the participating spectator, the last yards before the winning post seem to have a lurid green spot-light trained on them as the protagonists appear in the final scene before the curtain falls.

"He didn't get up, eh? How was it? The jockey left it too bloody late, didn't he?"

Manzini's muttering was the buzzing of a wasp close to Jacob's blanched, damp face.

"Was he beaten? That's what I'm asking you, Mr. Mac Gregor."

"It's a photograph. We've got to sit and suffer a bit longer."

Leave it still in doubt. Keep it quiet as long as possible. Hoard up the treasure. Say nothing apart from a nod exchanged with Corcoran and a low word of congratulation to Macey, as he took off the saddle in the winner's enclosure.

# NOCTURNE AT THE CABLE SHOP

On a summer evening Simeon lingered along Piccadilly looking into the closed shops with lit windows. At this fateful hour, almost any gadget was enough to catch his fancy and send him off on the imagining that was his daily bread, and which he would be starved of the moment he entered the office with the deceptively simple sign over it: 'Messengers and Theatre Tickets'.

Ben, tense from sleeplessness with the whole night still before him (he worked as a waiter at a club down the street, changing into his sombre black in the basement at seven a.m.), was on his high stool at the counter, checking by ear the first of the hourly calls of one of the old-fashioned brass machines behind him.

Simeon's last minute of freedom had been outside Cooks Travel Agency, and he hadn't quite come to himself from the deck of a barge quietly moored for the night on a broad river aglimmer with reflections from the lamps on the cobbled streets of the town on its bank.

Len, the other member of Simeon's staff of two, arrived a few minutes late and seemed more distressed than ever.

— My *colombe* has flown.

This 'dove', which he also referred to as 'my muse', was an enigma into which Simeon didn't like to enquire.

— She (should he have said 'it'?) will be back.

A rather tepid attempt at reassurance, but what could Simeon say without intruding?

— I've alerted the local police.

— You have?

Sweet Lord, what an inane remark, but Simeon was out of his depth.

— Heartless . . . Heartless . . . Heartless.

What was? Hopefully not his mindless comment. More likely still just the usual refrain about the desolation, disguished at daytime, of the late-night city. 'Not a stone laid on a stone with love; not a word spoken or an act committed except in the service of money.'

More of the security machines started up and a couple came in to send a cable which, though this they didn't know, would be collected by a motor cyclist on his nightly round several hours later and brought to an American cable company's offices. Simeon copied the text onto one of the company's forms, searched through the thick directory for the charge per word to the country to which it was directed, arrived at the total cost, rearrived at a different figure, was interrupted by a simultaneous clamour from two of the machines, returned to the couple who no doubt supposed these small brass monsters were receiving and despatching urgent messages all over the globe and that theirs was already on its way, announced a sum of half way between the two estimates, gave them their change and, regarding them for the first time, took a gratuitous dislike to them.

At two a.m. the girls from 'La Pigalle', a few doors away came running out, calling in shrill, twittering voices: 'taxi', the waiter from the Ritz called as always to change his pocketful of coins into notes, and from time to time the street girls appeared with cheques which they left for the messenger boys to take to the bank in the morning and the proceeds brought to their rooms later in the day, thus obviating the humilitation they felt they'd suffer from the bank clerks if going in person, not to mention the greater shame when the cheques, as could happen, turned out to be duds.

Then came the pale, tired-looking girl, as she did occasionally, to ask if she could rest on the bench in the basement where the messengers waited in the daytime to be called to the shop on an errand. Though strictly warned against complying by the day-manager, Simeon always agreed. She waited humbly while Simeon was busy rousing a security guard through the speaking tube attached to the machines whose signal was overdue. Then he accompanied her to the dank basement and unlocked the cupboard with its pile of rusty roller skates (on which in some distant past the boys skated through the comparitively empty streets), its old theatre posters and the sombre black uniform that Ben changed into each morning.

Four o'clock, the night fine and all still well. The racket

from the machines had eased off; it was getting light and late for major break-ins and burglaries, Simeon strolled up the empty street to buy a morning paper outside an all-night café near Leicester Square. When he had a few minutes quiet he would study the runners at Newmarket and thus, in a modest manner, start entering his imaginative kingdom again.

For this he had to wait until the vegetable lorries were passing on their way to Covent Garden, or sometimes later still when the office cleaners appeared with the pigeons.

Precisely at five-twenty-three (he was constantly alerted to the minute in case of overlooking a failed signal from a bank, a jewellery shop, warehouse or wherever the riches were stored) two men entered and asked for Leonard.

Simeon touched his shoulder as he bent over a machine, trying to decipher the indentations on the tape, with a gentleness that he didn't know he was capable of, though no doubt Len was unaware of it.

There was a small card in a plastic holder laid briefly on the counter and then Len was asking him to be present at the interview in the basement which the detectives, to which after hesitating, he agreed.

The rug had fallen from the girl stretched on the narrow bench as it was bound to, her face was to the wall.

— When last did you see her, Mr. Amhearst?

— At twilight yesterday, that is, by now, the day before, just a glimpse on the wing from the old apple tree to the sycamore in the garden.

— I'm speaking of your — ah . . . late companion.

— Late?

The sound Len made was not so much an intelligible word as the low cry of a trapped forest creature. Yes, Simeon's imagination was recovering from the nightly starvation.

— We appreciate that her untimely death has upset you.

At five-fifty, the poet, if that was what he was, left with them.

If anyone is interested, Simeon gave up the job soon after and, as an escape from basement-phobia, took a fifth-floor attic in a house in the industrial town of Roubaix in Northern France, not far from the First World War battlefields of Flanders across the Belgian frontier.

# 2016

The invitation was delivered by hand one fine September morning and it was signed: "Group Leader, Commandant XYZ".

He hadn't exactly been expecting it, but neither did it surprise him. For some time he had surmised that the airborne Groupies were not just an updated form of the youthful gangs who had been rampant around the middle of the previous century, such as the once notorious 'Mods and Rockers'. He didn't believe their purpose was merely harassing the leisure hours of the decent, propertied electorate who now formed over ninety percent of the community and voted en-bloc every four years for "The Coalition of all the Talents", as the permanent government was called. As allowed for in the system, the talents (if they ever existed) cancelled each other out and what remained was an inert body of legislators, kept, like the rest of the community, from unnecessary mental strain and worry by tranquilisers. They need never publicly open their mouths, the one assurance needed to calm the credulous mass of consumer-voters: "the situation is under constant review", having been taped and broadcast at regular intervals between the otherwise non-stop commercials.

When instant rocket-travel was innaugurated, with passengers packed sardine-wise into the padded tubes and so heavily sedated that they seldom fully came to themselves between flights, which averaged per family three a month, the Groupies had assembled aircraft, using parts discarded from the scrapped airline machines. The plane in which he was flown to Headquarters in the South where, rumor had it, an underground tank on the coast was kept filled with the otherwise unobtainable fuel by a sympathetic Arab state was powered by a Rolls Royce engine mounted below the tail wing with, defying accepted principles of engineering, as the Groupie defied most else, a petrol tank from an old Boeing 707 at the front.

The central hangar and offices, known as "The Pagan Place" because it was supposed to be the only building in Ireland on a wall of which an apparition hadn't appeared, was situated between two of the luxury hotels that had sprung up all over the place when the compressed air system of public transport was introduced. With weekly earnings in the region of eight hundred nylon punts, paper money had proven incapable of withstanding the constant handling in supermarkets open twenty-three hours a day and travel agents, where average families booked eighteen package tours a year, without naturally, being pre-informed of the itineraries.

He was told on arrival that he had been selected as one of the few independent writers left, who didn't work, that is, to the approved formula circulated to all members of "The National Institute of Irish Literary Practioners", which incidentally, ensured those that adhered to it at least six of the annual prizes that the members awarded each other. This formula was amended from time to time in accord with the reading public's, and the reviewers', requirements.

He was asked to correct the image of the Group of old-fashioned steam-mechanised drop-outs or weirdies, who were off the prescribed drugs needed for communal conformity in a high-speed, no friction society.

He certainly would, if told their programme.

They didn't like the word which was reminiscent of the economic programmes that ensured a continual rise in the standard of living with an accompanying, but uncharted, fall in the general level of intelligence of the imaginative kind.

Would he insert a small-print news item in the paper, between the mass of coloured ads and pages of T.V. schedules (there were now over a hundred indistinguishable stations to choose from, that they were planning a 1916 style, last ditch effort to alert the populace to the cosy cocoon of doom around them?

Tell him the proposed Proclamation and he'd do his best.

Oh, the day of proclamation is past, it's simply a matter of presenting a few questions for discussion.

O.K., Which ones?

Why, they must occur to someone like you all the time. If you tell us some of the popular assumptions you wouldn't mind seeing queried, they're bound to supplement ours.

Here goes: Is the family all it is supposed to be? Is the Church the answer? Does it either comfort the afflicted or afflict the comfortable?

You're on the right track though it's only a start.

I suppose you realise that if you suffer the fate of your prototypes and are marched off through the streets of the Capital from the G.P.O., not to the docks of course, but to a well-appointed institution in the midlands for incorrigible instigatiors of doubt and despondency, the section of the populace that can drag themselves from watching three commercials at the same time on their coloured T.V. triptych sets will spit on you even more venomously than on those before you.

# A TALE OF OLDEN TIMES

Harry knew that his long fiction could not be published at the time it was written in the early years of the century. It was before its day as are certain outstanding works of art that cross forbidden frontiers. Of course, he could be wrong, only time would tell.

The other person who had read it was a fellow patient at the same German mental clinic where Harry had gone because one of the doctors was Otto Laringer, a personal friend and associate of the great Sigmund Freud in Vienna.

Ivan was a Russian who claimed to have had close links with Dostoevsky, a writer who also had been before his time and was even now scarcely coming into his own in the recent English translations.

– One day your novel will be hailed as an original and daring work, Ivan had declared – but first must come the Russian Revolution that can't be long delayed (he had worked with an anti-Tsarist terrorist group before his illness and forced exile) and even after that it will take time to clear the stuffy air of Europe.

– How much time?

– Who knows? It may well require other upheavals and wars before the day of enlightenment dawns.

Harry was not impatient. He made enough money with his romances to pay for his stay at *Haus Eisenheim* as well as keep a room at the smart *Hotel Deutscher Kaiser* at nearby Bad Homburg where Dr. Laringer let him spend a few days now and then. Meanwhile, he was writing another novel for posterity. Assisted by Ivan, it was a sequel to the unfinished *Brothers Karamazov* in which the later life and adventures of Dmitri and Grusenka are followed. Their sexual relationship, only hinted at by the great Russian, he is describing in what would now be shocking and unacceptable detail. Both are extreme sensualists, in particular, the ex-street girl, Grusha, and at the same time visionaries, or at least Dmitri, and the resulting ferment disrupts all the old modes, assumptions and proprieties.

This forenoon Harry was enjoying his stroll among the palms in the *Kur Halle* on short leave from the establishment up in the Taunus hills. He sipped the sulphorous water from a mug engraved with what he supposed was the spa's coat of arms: a bird whose neck was ingeniously twisted under the handle and its beak about to grip the hand that held it.

This was not the cure he needed, just a relaxation after the other treatment, which according to Freud's associate was going so well. Was it though? Harry thought he knew differently. Oh, the old impulse to risk all in an attempt, before the time was ripe for his real and lasting triumph, to create a minor though shocking disruption to the horrible air of everlasting decorum, was as strong as ever.

— Drowning the vulture?

— Pardon?

He looked round at a girl in dark blue (bluebell-blue, ah, childhood innocence!) with a ribbon of the same hue in her straw hat and reflected once more in her frilled, folded parasol.

— That's what the habitués here call it, the vulture. Once it has got its beak into the liver it can only be made let go by constant draughts of this nasty water.

She spoke with the mewing modulations of London's West end.

— You don't look to me as if your liver was in any vulture-like grip.

A bold remark on first acquaintance, but Harry dealt in boldness and risk of a far more desperate sort.

— Oh, I'm not here for the cure. I'm accompanying my aunt, Katie Osborne.

Not as well-known as Mrs. Humphrey Woods, Mrs. Henry Ward, not to speak of Marie Corelli, Kate Osborne all the same was highly respected as a critic in the literary supplements of some English national newspapers.

— We're staying at the same hotel as you, Mr. Ruark, and she recognised you in the dining-room.

As what? Of course, he didn't ask. As the distinguished Irish novelist. Not, naturally, as the possessor of a dark and daunting secret.

— She thinks your books are not as widely read as they deserve.

— The blackbirds aren't chirping their titles from the hedges, that's true.

The light and easy tone. He'd become a master of it when needing to disguise the inner ferment.

He thought it best to move on with a slight bow. He had isolated himself from society, even from people of liberal moral attitudes, because even they would be unlikely to include in their tolerated categories of sexual aberrations his own particular form of delight.

But before he had completed his elegant little inclination of head and shoulders, grey Homburg doffed, she said: — Auntie thinks you must be here to work on a new novel.

— Ah.

Let them suppose anything rather than the actuality of the complex situation.

— She's dying to know if she's right and, if so, the direction your new romance is taking.

'Romance!', Christ save us, or, rather, me! But best leave it, Harry reflected.

— I'm engaged on a sequel to *The Brothers Karamazov,* Miss Osborne.

— I'm not Miss Osborne, she's my maternal auntie. My name's de Vere. Isn't that rather ambitious?

What? To have such a name with its vague aristocratic or, was it, theatrical associations? He was a little disorientated at the prolongation of the conversation. But, of course, she meant the project that he had revealed to her.

— Well, yes and no, Miss de Vere. (Not Vera de Vere? No, he supposed not. Nor Bluebell de V., either).

— You feel an affinity to the great Russian?

She had heard of him (good for her), although translations of his great novels had only lately begun to appear and without much acclaim. (The blackbirds, not to mention the thrushes, weren't warbling their praises either, ha, ha!)

— An affinity, you could say so. But more than that, I'm a friend of Ivan's.

— Pardon?

— Of Ivan Karamazov.

Better let her take him for a literary eccentric, put her off the scent of his real alienation.

— You identify with this great fictitious character?

— When he was writing the novel in 1880, Ivan Karamazov was in his early thirties which makes him now, let's see, about fifty five. Though he looks more.

— You mean, Mr. Ruark, you've met the person on whom the famous character was based?

— Put it like that if you please. He's living not far from here, in the Taunus.

— Quite extraordinary! This will excite Auntie no end. Tell me, Mr. Ruark, would it be possible that you arrange a meeting? Or am I presuming on too brief an acquaintanship and one, I admit, of my own arranging.

Why not! What a temptation. A drive through the countryside with the two ladies! Better excuse himself straight away before the idea took possession of him.

But it was too late. Once his imagination had been sufficiently excited to transform what remained usually as no more than fantasy into possible actuality, there could be no holding back.

This had been explained to him by Dr. Otto Laringer under whose care he was at the clinic and Otto, they were on Christian names terms, had said that according to the theories of the eminent Viennese, Harry's libido, as he called it, had been diverted, he used these, to Harry, unreal expressions, in early childhood.

He well knew the risk, but it ws that that increased the obsession. His hidden joy on the one hand, on the other, society's contemptuous dismissal of it as self-exposure and exhibitionism, terms equally inadequate to him as those Otto used.

Oh, it was part of the generative mystery of nature, the bursting out of the bud, the blade, the shoot from winter's hiddenness. But mankind, more shame to it, had got used to the shock of Spring, society was outraged by the bursting forth of male flesh except in the most private and approved circumstances.

The shattering vibration as of a powerful spring whose base was in his spine, released the shame, the exultation and the wild hope that the reverbations would cross the gulf between him and the fashionably attired, tightly bodiced woman (elderly, middle-aged, youngish, who cared). That would be the deepest, most devasting satisfaction it was in his gift to imagine. He has already gambled away so much on the hundred-to-one chance in various places, the more unsuitable the better, brightly lit drawing-rooms at afternoon tea time, reserved enclosures at summer race-meetings, but never in darkened cinemas or suchlike holes and corners. That would have been tame and ignominious as were to him the usual satisfactions by gradual leading up and sensual persuasion, ending in private, shockless love-making.

Ah, how banal life was becoming! The novels and poems reflected it, pure skimmed milk and rosewater! His own in the forefront, but that was because he needed the money. Without a lot of it his situation would be even more hopeless than it was. But he had a couple of typescripts locked in the drawer of his bedside commode which would explode like anarchists' bomb-shells were they to be printed. One day, if he lived long enough, he believed they might release in a few undomesticated and even uncivilised breasts visions close to his own.

When he was introduced to Kate Osborne, statuesque, fiftyish, by her niece that evening at the *Hotel Deutsche Kaiser* over coffee and brandy, for which he had joined them at their table, he suggested an outing to the Taunus hills for the following day.

They set out in a landau on a sunny morning, the horse wore a silken hood against the flies and the ladies carried sunshades, Miss Osborne and Harry on the rear seat and Miss de Vere, in flowered muslin, with her back to the coachman. Their knees were covered by a light cashmere rug without which, Kate Osborne confided in him, she never travelled in foreign parts.

– Very sensible, Harry remarked.

Good sense, good breeding and propriety were part of the elegant scene, which aroused in him the more urgent desire to disrupt it.

Clip-clop past stretches of tawny maize and fields brimming with golden sunflowers 'that count the steps of the sun, seeking for that sweet golden clime where the traveller's journey is done,' as he was counting those of the horse, deciding that when he reached ninety he would risk all and take the plunge (not an appropriate simile, but he was beyond literary niceties). But he was interrupted by the approach of another conveyance and a brisker set of hoof-beats. A smart phaeton with a cockaded driver and, beside him, a portly bearded figure in morning coat and top hat, was approaching.

– The Monarch! Kate Osborne exclaimed as it was about to pass and gravely inclined her head under the large picture hat. The girl also bowed although with less dignity and grace, and Harry, slow to react to the outwardly passing scene, raised his Homburg at the last moment. King Edward, the Peacemaker, as Miss Osborne murmured, as though letting them into a secret, he was beginnng to be called, touched the curled brim of his topper with a gloved finger in gracious acknowledgement.

Kingly decorum! His passing had heightened the sense of utter rectitude and immaculate manners on which high society and great civilisations are founded.

At this critical (for Harry) moment Miss Bluebell Vera de Vere said she would like to get out and walk the last part of the slight incline to lighten the load fro the horse and stretch her legs (no indeliacy could be detected by the strictest stickler).

Harry had sometimes been filled with joy when he saw how a tiny weed had thrust its way through cement, perhaps even caused the crack, in a garden path. Now the moment had come for the same universal force in him to burst through the social and moral barriers of time and place. He twitched a corner of the rug from his knees and having already undone the necessary buttons, lent back slightly to, as it were, make way for the appearance of the regal, life-giving presence before his companion.

She saw it at once, how could she not? No chance to pretend a distant point in the landscape had caught her attention. For a moment all, his whole future and past too (for if the life-force within him failed to crack the psychic cement then all his dreams were vain) was at desperate risk.

She slipped off the pearl-grey glove from her hand, in what he sensed was a semi-trance, and grasped the warm-to-burning, monstrous stem of the tree of brute energy.

Dr. Laringer invited them to coffee and *Kuchen* in the guest room at the clinic. At Miss de Vere's request the patient known as Ivan Karamazov appeared, formally attired as usual in long frock coat, tight fawn trousers and Russian-style blouse with a high, buttoned neck, beneath which was wound a white, silk kerchief. He wore *pincenez.*

Otto Laringer brought Harry to his study.

— My God, it's happened! You've gone and exposed yourself!

— How do you know?

— Why, by your face, of course. The nervous tension, the lines I thought were permanently engraved there, are gone.

— Rejoice with me, Otto.

Rejoice? Where did it take place? Don't tell me in a crowded *Kur Halle* before the élite of Europe as I believe you'd planned but thought would never have the courage for. Oh, what a dusaster! It will damage the good name of *Haus Eisenheim* irretrievably when it's known you had permission to take a room at the *Deutscher Kaiser.*

'I had the privilege of meeting Mr. H. Ruark in Germany,' Kate Osborne wrote in her syndicated column.' With the assistance of a Russian friend of his who knew Dostoevsky in his youth, Mr. Ruark has undertaken to complete the unfinished story of *The Brothers Karamazov.* From what I know of this underrated novelist, his sequel will lack nothing of the inspiring earthiness of the great original.'

# THE STORMY PETREL

When I came back through the hall from cleaning the room
assigned to the rabbits, the long white envelope with the
foreign-looking crest on the flap lay on the carpet. That's it;
yes, my gentle creatures – I was pretending to be communing
with the animals rather than have to admit that at such
moments I tended to talk to myself – the invitation has come
and is safely in my hands.

A pleasant prospect: a dip in a blue-enamelled (was tiled
the word I wanted here?) pool before the six-o'clock apertif,
strong, pale, aromatic, followed by dinner on the seaward
side, candlelight sparkling on cut-glass decanters (instead of
on the cut-price bottle of wine that was my usual weekly treat)
and on the sensationally white flesh farmed in the V (for
Venus) of plunging necklines. For all of which I didn't give an
ass's fuck! The real cause of the exictement that was going to
my head and making me raise my voice as if addressing the
rodents two rooms away was that I could now enact in my
imagination the scene in my host's book-lined (when carried
away I resort to clichés) study.

How many others among my colleagues had received a
similar convocation? Quite a number as it turned out. Many are
called but few chosen. Amen to that! Nobody could say later
that the net hadn't been spread wide and all the small fry carefully weighed and even in some cases measured before being
found wanting; nobody, that is except the cranks and bloody
begrudgers.

A train ticket (first class) was clipped to the ambassadorial
invitation but from the rail-head there was still a long road to
the mansion. Some went by hired car (fare to be defrayed on
arrival), two or three started out on foot, hoping, no doubt,

to be picked up en route, dusted down, and shown the extra respect accorded those who voluntarily take the lower places. And, if my eyes didn't deceive me (there I go again!), I saw our reverend Arts Councillor perched sideways on the rump of a briskly-trotting jennet.

To vary the style with a touch of the question-and-answer technique: what transport did the central figure select? A bloody boat. Extravagant? All kind of extravaganzas are fully justified when the stakes are really high: Motto fastened with a safety pin over my four-poster. Seriously though, I needed time to take myself in hand; I, narrator of grim adventures, survivor, if not hero, of bloody, interior battles, had still at this last hour, to prepare myself for what looked like being one of my most difficult private struggles.

The possiblity was there, perhaps the probability; I didn't want to follow it that far . . . not yet. Naturally, it had got round: what the purpose of the house-party was. We all, even the most unlikely candidates for high honour, felt a certain awe, realising that it was a matter of political expediency for the donors this year to choose an aspirant from this blessed hand of ours for the *Grand Prix,* triple bar.

What better setting in which to come to myself after the dizzy dreams of the last days than the deck of a small, but sturdy, pitching craft, gripping a rope, the right leg of my jeans, later both, my upper part being shielded by raincoat, salty-soaked?

As soon as the sloop was beyond the headland, off-black swells began overtaking us from a, to me, unexpected quarter and catching us three-quarter beam on. (I have my own nautical style).

I had to choose one of two possible responses if the . . . should it happen that . . . in case the elegant diplomat approached me, drink in hand (*mine,* he was said to be abstemious). First: the one I longed with all my heart to be able to decide on. It would be a matter of adopting a taken-aback, two-parts genuine, one-part phony (with a light sprinkling of respectfulness) air, accepting gratefully but preserving a mental loophole so that when the official announcement was made I'd have both the glory and the additional and more select glory of refusing the first glory!

Fantastic! I shivered, not in the watery chill but in the semi-sensual anticipation. Two up and one to play, or, for the non-golfer, bursting out of the ruck with a furlong to cover!

Second (and this would be hard to the point of . . . leave it, I'm no good at metaphors): tell our immaculately attired host when he laid his hand on the shoulder of my not-so-immaculate (though clean) summer jacket that, while I was overwhelmed, etcetera and so on, it must be a simple No and I prefereed that no mention in any media in any country be made of my refusal, as, no doubt, would also suit the illustrious donors. Let the fact that I was declining the piece of pie with the iced sultana at the centre (so it was said, only the recipients actually knew what was there) remain a secret between me and them.

Did I know the right choice for me (this is not a tale about anyone else)? Yes. Was I going to make it? Let's put it like this; was I going to swallow the lollipop, wrapping and all, if I got the chance, before the Committee Chairman had time to let go the ribbon? Yes!

Then it was that the tall, sober-jawed mate at the tiller, who hadn't yet opened his mouth said something that the wind took away before I could catch it.

'Eh?'

A jerk of his head towards the shelter of the hatch that led to the cabin.

'It's O.K.'

Flitting down one of the shadowy valleys overtaking us I saw this small, black spectre, soon to be the only heart-tick and drop of blood-warmth as the dusk fell on the salt desolation when we were gone.

Omens, warnings, come to those who in their dilemma seek them with a pure heart. But also to those who, no matter how heart-sullied, have the gift of turning make-believe into reality; can make themselves feel and believe what they know is true.

This little fowl of the species that thirst-crazed, ship-wrecked mariners used to call Mother Carey's chickens (as they were transported perhaps to summer evenings at home) was communicating to me in my need: Where I go you will have once to venture, in the chill gales that blow day and night in these parts. Or again: 'No impedimenta hung round the neck nor fastened to the wing-tips are anything but fatal in these latitudes.

The sloop slipped into a new pattern-motion; the waves, like a series of too-soft, old brooms that cannot rid a carpet of a splinter except little by little in a succession of sweeps, kept thrusting under the boat and tossing us a little further on.

O, my secret albatross, my marine black-bird with the speck of white (that I first took to be foam) on the rump, and the disproportionately long wings, teach me how not to wait!

For news, for the morning post, for an answer; I must learn to fly just aloft of the storm, but not out of it, to float and ride the wet-ash swells as dawn breaks, head tucked under oily wing.

Who still wants to know the outcome of the story. Anyone who does hasn't bothered to read it.

# THE MAN WHO WENT TO THE MOON AND BEYOND UNDER HIS OWN STEAM

Things had changed; no more fulfilment of ancient prophecies, no learned doctors anxious to listen and compare; not much of a welcome for such as he.

Julius Mariner, in his late twenties (his actual birthday was not celebrated and possibly not exactly known), applied for a job at the local Zoological Gardens and was taken on as cleaner and assistant handyman in the large carnivori extension. This gave him satisfaction and was a boost to his morale although he was not sure what the word 'carnivori' portended. Previously apprenticed to a carpenter, he had later failed to find employment in the trade and had spent a long time on the dole.

The company of the big cats seemed to suit him and their roars at feeding time was music to his ears, although he winced at the noises of heavy traffic  and particularly at the strident tones of most of the voices on television that reached a shriek in the commercials. He carried out his rather menial tasks to the satisfaction of his superiors.

He became attached to an old lioness called Magda, considered vicious by the two keepers, and, quite remarkably, she to Julius. With the key to the iron hatches through which he raked out the cages, he could raise hers of an evening and creep under it. For two whole weeks he slept curled up between her front and hind legs, his head on the tawny fur of her belly, saving a fortnight's rent though this, needless to say, didn't enter his mind. All this was unknown to the night watchman who never came beyond the porch on his rounds.

He visited other parts of the Gardens in his spare time, especially the reptile house, fascinated apparently by the pythons, cobras, boas and black mambas. He had also a soft spot for the rodents.

In the end, he lost his job, not for fraternisation with the beasts or any failure in the carrying out of his obscure tasks, but in the general recession.

He was given an excellent reference by the superintendent, the first and only one he was ever to gain, and he treasured it, pinning it to the wall of the small room in a back street where he lived with a small furry creature that he had taken from a litter whose exact species he didn't know, rearing this somewhat fierce little animal on the cheaper cuts of butcher's meat and milk. He spent a lot of time caring for it ( it was unexpectedly delicate) and only when it was full grown, though not large, did he apply for another job. After several failures, which it was not in his nature to take to heart, he applied, apparently on an impulse, to the National Space Agency. He passed both an oral and written examination on astro-physics (which he had given as his special subject) and was then asked which of the three departments he had in mind: Ground, Lunar or Interstellar.

Always tending toward the middle or centre position, the second of three persons, the meat in the sandwich, the in-between malefactor, he chose the Lunar.

A week or so passed without further development and the matter more or less slipped from his mind and then on his return to his room one evening he found a partially shredded manilla envelope that the landlady had slipped under the door. Polly, as he called the small beast, had gnawed up a good part of the document appointing him assistant to the moon-mapping section of the Department.

After less than a year at the Agency, Julius had been twice promoted and had gained the unusual privilege of being allowed to bring Polly to the office where, being a night creature, she slept on a piece of folded linen under his desk. She was left alone by the clerks and secretaries after showing a disinclination to being petted.

Then one day came a call to the Deputy Head of the Agency's topfloor office.

— I won't beat about the bush, Mr. Mariner, but inform you straight off that, in competition with several of our most suitably gifted staff, you've been chosen as a participator in our coming lunar probe.

— My humble duty, Sir Patrick.

Oh, Julius had an old-world, though by no means inelegant, way of conducting himself in the highest intellectual circles. What his thoughts were, or how far he'd anticipated this outcome, is hard to say. From later developments though, one may assume he meant to take Polly with him and that he didn't intend entering a module or space capsule for the voyage. He did however submit to several weeks training with the other two selected astronauts and to being fitted out with helmet and space suit for the projected trip by moonmobile around the SEA OF TRANQUILITY. He humbly submitted himself to all the procedures, the measurings, the adjustments, the sealings-off, the breathing tests, the oxygen readings, aware that he had need of nothing like this.

After subjecting himself to these earthly techniques for weeks, on one of the last evenings Julius, alone with Polly at supper in his room, having dipped a morsel of meat in the goblet of wine he was drinking and given it to the furred creature, quoted a line of scripture: 'The light shone through darkness and darkness comprehended it not.' Did the beast comprehend it? Had the old lioness? There is no telling, at least not here.

Julius Mariner did not wait for the official blast-off which, incidentally, had twice to be postponed, once due to the weather and then to a technical malfunction. He set out, accompanied by Polly, one cloudy evening in early June, seemingly at walking pace, although in terms of celestial movement, at a speed four times that of light, slowing down almost immediatly to allow, perhaps, those whom he had chosen as company for part of the journey to catch up with him.

These, speaking foolishly or from our humdrum angle, as St. Paul puts it, were a mixed lot. One or two I even hesitate to name for fear of not being believed, and thus exposing the well-intentioned reader to the charge of lack of faith.

A pale, plump girl was one of the first to reach him. She turned down the collar of her dark travelling cloak, of an old-fashioned cut, freeing the lower part of her face and touching Julius Mariner's cheek with her lips.

– Whom have we here, Master?

A natural question, even if there was nobody at the moment to put it. Later, among the small company that had gathered, names were mentioned: Thérèse of Lisieux, patron saint of

France, Grushenka, Fanny Brawne (surprisingly), Mary Magdalen (predictably), another of the Gospel Marys, the Blessed Juliana, Emily Brontë.

Mostly, as the crowd grew, it was evident that most of them were, or had been, of no great public significance. Many looked surprised and ill at ease, wondering perhaps whether they were being made fools of and ridiculed. A change, however, soon came over them as they got their sea, or space, legs, and even those women, scantily dressed and embarrased, as if hastily dragged from their beds, were soon tagging along and chatting together.

— Hey, Boss, what about a pic-nic?

The suggestion came from, to use an old-world expression that went with his appearance and garb, an ill-favoured looking rogue.

— Ah, Pius, you were always a guzzler, Julius told him, not at all put out.

A little later there was indeed a halt for refreshments.

— Don't say it's fish again!

— Shut your big blasphemous mouth!

— What about a litre of old Algerian?

— With due respect, I'll make do with a keg from the vineyards of Galile.

There was a scuffle when a cur tried to take a chunk of raw cod from Polly who was onto the dog in a flash and would probably have bitten deep into its throat had not Julius whispered a word to the rodent. The dog retreated with something substantial in its mouth and Polly returned to her undiminished piece of raw fish.

There was this young woman who, at first glance, with her rather staring eyes and dark stains under them, her defiant and yet demoralised air, might have been a back-street abortionist. She had an American accent, of the deep south tonality, and had once written out of despair: 'There was no Fall because there was nothing to fall from and no Redemption because there was no Fall and no Judgement because there wasn't the first two. Nothing matters but that Jesus was a liar.'

This was someone called Flannery O'Connor, and if not exactly a cripple, she was obviously not in the best of health. After welcoming her with especial warmth, Julius sent her to the two women who were distributing food and drink. After the pic-nic he dismissed the company and within the hour had stepped onto the moon where he remained long enough for Polly to give birth to her litter.

Note: One of the astraonauts who landed a few weeks later, when temporally separated from his companion, saw, in a shallow ravine, several small rat-like creatures that disappeared down a crevice. This he never reported, fearing to be supposed to have been hallucinating.

Julius Mariner's further voyage took him out of earthly records and history, which are anyhow sketchy in his regard, and into others. Whether these will one day be collected into a Holy Scripture and opened on Doomsday, probably a quite ordinary day in all other respects, is, with only our present presience to guide us, impossible to predict.

For my part what obsesses me is the daily life of Julius on this planet, in his various jobs (three as far as I've been able to trace them), his periods of apparent idleness, his vigils and occasional feasts, his rare correspondence (I've discovered four letters, two of them applications for jobs) and his few notebook jottings.

# From a novel FAILLANDIA

Waking at six-thirty I'm washed, dressed and having breakfast of *café-au-lait,* a boiled duck egg (our concierge keeps a dozen waterfowl of the Peking species), wheaten bread and honey by soon after seven. I'm not a food faddist and would as soon have a slice from the white loaf with plenty of butter and marmalade but the madame downstairs arranges a weekly delivery of basic comestibles and I leave the choice to her. (My domestic arrangement, it could be said, should be kept out of a factual report of this kind but by a familiar down-to-earth background a sense of actuality can be, I think, achieved.)

This morning, though, having finally got home and to bed at three a.m., I'd set the alarm for eight o'clock. Black coffee and no duck egg with an anxious scanning of the newspaper. 'Night of Terror'. (An exaggeration, of course). 'Bombs explode in Newspaper Offices'. 'Several Defused' (one actually). 'Curfew imposed on City' and 'Army takes over Security'.

I read the columns of smaller print. Nothing about the device at the offices that the lieutenant in charge of the bomb squad had told me they were taking away with them for examination. So much the better. I want *Faillandia* to be kept out of all this. It being a repository from all this publicity that might strip away the protective shadows in which its more meditative readers were at home.

Unusual sounds from the usually quiet and leafy side street. From my fourth floor living room window I saw a couple of long, grey-coated motor cyclists were stopped in the centre of the roadway opposite the entrance to the block of flats, their jack-booted feet on the asphalt, the engines running. What did they herald? No, I'm not attempting to work up an artificial sense of expectancy. To read about the sequence of events is one thing but to experience them as they followed each other is another.

There then appeared from under the canopy of tenderly green, young leaves a sqat, grey car, a triangular pendant with a black star on a red background sprouting from the front of the bennet.

A last look round the room and a glance in the cupboard to confirm there were drinks in plenty and also an impulse to swallow a small brandy, quickly dismissed. A knock on the apartment door which I opened to a tall young man in a black suit on the lapel of which was a medaillion with the same symbol as had flown from the car. He introduced himself by a name a syllable of which I didn't take in and added something which might have been 'at your service', but I very much doubt it. He then stood aside as Colonel Klotz steepped from the lift (in which he'd been waiting? Or had the *aide de camp* ran up the stairs before him? An athletic-looking type, he could have done so and not been out of breath).

Klotz was wearing an undisguised grey army uniform on which were no ribbons, not a medal or medaillion, only three faded silver stripes across the shoulder straps.

— Good morning, Mr. Spokane.

— Honoured.

Perhaps that's not what I answered, because it certainly wasn't how I felt.

I took him into the sitting-room, followed by the *aide de camp,* bodyguard, secretary, and instead of choosing the comfortable chair I'd set out, he sat in an upright one at the table, forcing me to take a similar one at the other side while the young man sat in one of the arm chairs.

— There you are, Paul, the Colonel said to him — I told you there was sure to be plenty of books. As you know, Mr. Spokane, I'm not a well-educated person, never are, we Generals, Colonels and Corporals, though some of us, like Hindenburg and Pétain, whose prestige was won on the battlefield, know how to conduct themselves in a dignified way.

What was this? His way of informing me of the new *situation?* Had he *'taken over',* and if so what? The responsibility for law and order? The armed forces? The government?

— De Gaulle was a man of culture from the start.

Don't just stare at him in surprise or curiosity. Say something that was neither a flat contradiction of his statement nor a flaccid agreement.

— Franco and de Gaulle were much of a muchness except in one vital respect, both church-goers and utter traditionalists in the old national-saviour sense, de Gaulle called in and consulted France's outstanding writers, as 'the conscience of the nation,' while in Franco's Spain they were banished or killed. Isn't that so, Captain?

— Roughly, although de Gaulle never forgave the collaborators, and some, like Céline, were condemned to death.

— Céline, who's she?

I had an inkling of the mind of Klotz and of the ambition and ferocious urge for power it shared with these historic figures.

— There was a similar difference between Stalin and Hitler, the Colonel went on — fate was against the great Slav leader (it plays the decisive part in these mysterious affairs) and he never managed to get his Russian intelligentsia behind him.

— He didn't make much of an attempt, I put in.

— Wait a minute, we'll come to that. He was in awe of the priests and priestesses of great art, of which it seems there were a number in the land, as the jumped-up Austro-German Corporal never was.

— Basically, Hitler was a nobody, that's true, a banal, gossipy old woman. Tie an apron round his waist and he'd have looked the part.

— You think so, Spokane? If he'd managed to impose his New Order on the West it wouldn't have been a cosy, old woman's one for a lot of people, eh Paul?

Our eyes met, the Captain's and mine. One of the damned and chosen race, I could have talked to him of matters undreamed of by Colonel Klotz, yet he had picked him out, as he had selected me, as a possible collaborator.

— Imaginative intelligence doesn't go with war lords, I suggested.

— And without it history's final approval is withheld. Am I right?

This time the Colonel looked at me. I had to laugh, although it was risky, I didn't yet know him all that well. But he burst out laughing too.

— You literary lot are just as much concerned with what

history makes of you, if you ask me.

— Maybe so, Colonel, but they (I don't include myself in your category) try to change sensibilities, not maps. Even Stalin never dreamed of that.

— Stalin might have, hadn't it been for an unlucky chance. You know the history of how he got on the phone to the best Russian writer then alive (the Colonel paused and the *aide de camp* murmured 'Boris Pasternak' with a smile that could have meant: 'If I'd said 'Dostoevsky' he'd be none the wiser', or more likely: 'which he, Pasternak, wasn't, but let it pass'), well, yes, this evidently somewhat timid character, to get his opinion on other members of the Russian intelligentsia, especially a certain outstanding poet who was proving uncooperative. And this Pasternak character, taken by surprise, made no attempt to make a case for his friend, so that Stalin told him: 'I though you'd stick up for your colleagues', and rang off, leaving the much-admired writer white-faced and trembling.

We had printed the authentic account of the incident in an article on Mandelstram in *Faillandia* which Klotz must have read.

— If the Little Father of All the Russians had found somebody with the guts and the faith in his calling to make a case for the poets and soothsayers ('soothsayers' was how Stalin probably thought of them with awe because he had more than a bit of peasant superstition in him) he'd have listened, and who knows what it would have led to!

Holy Christ, what was that? Not what it might have led to, but the faint chirping from the next room but one.

Pieta's sick bird, her wounded Dove of Peace, whose healing meant the world to her.

Rising late, more distressed than hungover, swallowing gulps of black coffee, scanning the scarey headlines, with noises in my head and from the street, not having come to myself enough to register the former as the bird's cry for nourishment, I'd neglected it.

One of the moments of truth, no use pretending otherwise.

Pasternak had had his and failed miserably. He had tried to get Stalin back on the phone a few moments later but there was a negative response from the Kremlin. No second chance is every vouchafed.

— Please excuse me, Colonel, Pieta Dolgorouky, a part-time member of the magazine's staff (why the unecessary detail? My nerve failed me like Pasternak's, but I kept on) left me a sick creature to care for when she went to hospital.

— A what?

— A bird, a fledgling.

I left the room before he had time to question further. On my way through the hall there was a ring at the apartment door. Frank Everek stood there, miraculously, when I opened it.

— Good morning, Boss.

Several hours before I'd given him a job distributing the magazine in some of the more prosperous suburbs which, as I only grasped later, gave him an opportunity of getting to know the lie of the land without any obvious hanging about. It was only when I heard of the armed robbery at Eitel's villa (the owner of amusement arcades along the sea front) that I realised the connection. Not that Frank had denied it to me. He had also mentioned that some of the bored housewives in the luxury apartment blocks had not been averse to letting him slip in instead of putting the package through the letter box.

— I believe you've got his Nibs here?

— In the front room.

He did not bat an eyelid. A coot cat, Kathy had called him. He had seen the military in the street, passed the sentries no doubt posted on each floor.

— What about getting my old job back?

— The magazine has been banned.

— I know that, Boss. All the more need for distributors if you can't sell it in the shops.

— It may not come to that. That's why Klotz is here, to see if we can come to a compromise.

Frank gave me a look that I didn't like. Just released from a three year (was it?) stretch, who, for Christ's sake, was he to sit in judgement!

— I've a job for you right away.

I showed him the cardboard box, the tin of cat's food, the sharpened match stick, and opened the lid. The bird hopped onto the edge of the box, held its head on one side, took a long beady look at the stranger, who held out his forefinger. With it firmly fastened there I conducted Frank to the front room when I could overlook the operation entrusted to him.

Klotz was at the window, looking out, and the Captain, I thought, saying something to placate him. As we came in he was on his feet in a second and (I won't say reaching for his hidden gun, not just because the phrase is hackneyed but because I'm not sure it would be true), very much on the alert at the sight of Frank and the box I carried.

I made the introduction as brief as possible. It was unlikely that the name would mean anything to Klotz or that, if he had seen a photo of Frank in the papers at the time of the trial, he would recall it. The Captain might, but I had a feeling he would do nothing to circumvent the purpose of his visit.

— Give Paul a ring when you've made up your mind, Mr. Spokane.

— About what, Colonel?

I wanted it clear. But that was not to be.

— About whether you're willing to discuss with him conditions for the ban on your magazine to be lifted.

If only he knew we had intended to continue publishing clandestinely! Here was a possible solution to what was a desperate decision, into which Pieta had talked me.

As soon as they were gone, I hurried to the hospital with the good news. A nurse showed me to the ward where Pieta lay unconscious, a plastic bottle of blood plasma above her head with a cannula from it that disappeared under her bandaged wrist.

I moved the tall bedside table on rubber castors and pulled up a chair to the bed. On it were a glass of cloudy liquid with a straw in it and a small, leather-framed photo of myself.

I was touched, and shocked. Guilt-stricken, might be nearer the mark. No more prevarication would work. At least I had been spared, *she* had been spared more like, my announcement of 'the good news' which (better face it) would have come as a betrayal.

— Pieta.

A losening of the corners of her mouth but then the pale lips regained their line of repose.

Nurses flitted by on white noiseless wings in the shape of shoes, an old crone mumbled a litany of holy names and complaints, another, spoon-fed against her will, gurgled and denounced the young sister.

Beyond the tall window birds were flying into and out of a large dark tree, perhaps an ilex, against a brass-coloured sky. My fingers rested on the back of the hand into whose wrist the blood plasma was being conducted (how dark it is! Give me your little paw).

A constant traffic of birds out of the sky and into the huge shadow with its halo of yellow light.

Against all likelihood, solace descended on the white bed, with its upturned, suspended bottle, the high mobile table and what was on it.

I scribbled a note: 'The fledling is recovering, the tail feathers are growing,' folded it and left it under the glass.

That was the good news. There was no other.

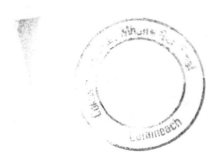